TRIVIA
and MORE TRIVIA

TRIVIA and MORE TRIVIA

by
Dan Carlinsky
and
Edwin Goodgold

CASTLE BOOKS

About the Authors

Edwin Goodgold and Dan Carlinsky began the Trivia craze in America with a series of intercollegiate Trivia contests and the first books on the game. Besides this volume, they have collaborated on *Rock 'n' Roll Trivia* and several other books, as well as numerous humor articles for the Sunday New York Times. Mr. Goodgold is also author of *I Spy* and *To Be Continued ...* (with Ken Weiss). Mr. Carlinsky's other books include *A Century of College Humor* and *Bicycle Tours In and Around New York* (with David Heim).

AUTHORS' NOTE

It all began, we assume, when Adam and Eve were sitting around the garden one night with nothing much to do. Suddenly, Eve got one of her many bright ideas. "Let's play Trivia," she said seductively, and she cast a covetous glance in the direction of Adam.

"We can't," Adam sighed as he loosened a notch on his fig leaf. "Nothing's happened yet."

"You're right," Eve answered. "I guess there's nothing we can do but wait."

And so they waited patiently—or maybe not so patiently, for shortly thereafter were born to them two sons, Cain and Abel. Exactly what happened next nobody really knows, but from then on the begetting was fierce.

More than 3,000 years after the first unsuccessful attempt at a game of Trivia, Herodotus recorded, in a yet-to-be-published holograph, an extraordinary conversation that took place in front of Loew's Sparta. Several theatergoers, it seems, were engaged in a terrific argument as to who had starred in a Cretan summer-stock production of *Lysistrata* eleven years earlier. Wonder of wonders—Trivia had been rediscovered!

7

Since the time of the ancient Greeks, the mental and spiritual exercise called Trivia has been enjoyed by every generation. The nuclear age, however, has seen the haphazard practice of the game made into a socially recognized art.

Like all progressive movements, the Trivia movement has been sparked by youth. Students who fall asleep over Aristotle, Rembrandt, Proust and differential calculus have been known to salivate and quietly whine when challenged to relive briefly their Trival heritage. Questions such as "What were the names of Superman's parents on Krypton?", "Who is the Lone Ranger's nephew?" and "What are the words to the Bosco jingle?" seem to be more powerful than a locomotive in producing emotional responses to the non-monumental yet nostalgic events of those thrilling days of yesteryear.

Organized Trivia got its start at Columbia College in New York City, where students have watched a parlor game develop into an institution. Today, the phenomenon of Trivia has, sure as shootin', swept the entire nation. People everywhere have been challenging one another with questions about the Thin Man's dog, the inhabitants of Allen's Alley and Aunt Fritzie's boyfriend. The holder of a Black Belt in Trivia is admired today as much as the owner of a Captain Midnight Secret Decoder Ring.

This book contains only a few hundred of many thousands of memories we have seen arouse people in all walks of life—regardless of race, religion, place of national origin or fan-club affiliation. It is only appropriate that we mention those without whom our work would have been impossible: Walt Disney, Fran Striker, David Sarnoff, Mr. and Mrs. Arthur Lack, Jack Benny, and Elmer Fudd.

EDWIN GOODGOLD,
DAN CARLINSKY
New York City, November, 1965

abbott and costello	What were the first names of ABBOTT and COSTELLO?
aldrich, henry	What book was HENRY ALDRICH's friend Homer always reading?
allen's alley	Who lived in ALLEN'S ALLEY?
allen, steve	The three original men in the street on *THE STEVE ALLEN SHOW* were————.
amos 'n' andy	What was theme song of *AMOS 'N' ANDY?*
	What were the names of Sapphire Stevens' brother and sister?
	What organization did George Stevens head as the Kingfish?
andrews, archie	Which two girls are the objects of ARCHIE ANDREWS's affections?
	Who is the coach at Archie's school?
animal	Who played ANIMAL in the movie *Stalag 17?*

abbott and costello	Bud (William) and Lou
aldrich, henry	*How to Win the Love of a Good Woman*
allen's alley	Titus Moody, Senator Claghorn, Mrs. Nussbaum and her husband Pierre, Falstaff Openshaw, and Ajax Cassidy
allen, steve	Louis Nye (Mad. Ave.'s Gordon Hathaway), Tom Poston (the forgetful one), N. D. Knotts (N. D., of course, standing for Nervous Don)
amos 'n' andy	"The Perfect Song"
	LeRoy and Opalette
	Mystic Knights of the Sea (Tim Moore, you remember, played the Kingfish on television.)
andrews, archie	Betty (the blonde) and Veronica (the seductress)
	Coach Cleats (who probably kept his job only because he was Mr. Weatherbee's nephew)
animal	Robert Strauss

10

atomic drop   What west-coast wrestler invented the ATOMIC DROP?

autry, gene   Sing the first two lines of GENE AUTRY's theme song.

Who was Gene's sidekick on television?

What all-time great record hit was first recorded by Gene on Columbia and later done by Bing Crosby and many others?

bad seed   Who played the child lead in *THE BAD SEED?*

bagdasarian   Who is ROSS BAGDASARIAN?

barbella   Who was CORPORAL BARBELLA?

bardot, brigitte   What big movie brought BRIGITTE BARDOT before the receptive American public's eyes?

atomic drop

Dangerous Danny McShane (No, it wasn't Barry Goldwater.)

autry, gene

"I'm back in the saddle again,
Out where a friend is a friend . . ."

Pat Buttram

"Rudolph the Red-Nosed Reindeer"

bad seed

Patty McCormack, who also played Ingeborg on *I Remember Mama* (if you really want to get trivial!)

bagdasarian

the guy who recorded himself at 33⅓ so he would sound like a chipmunk at 45 rpm's—David Seville

barbella

one of Sergeant Bilko's many flunkies (played by Harvey Lembeck)

bardot, brigitte

And God Created Woman

12

batman   BATMAN's butler was————.
          What was the relationship be-
          tween Robin and Batman
          when they were not the "dy-
          namic duo"?
          In what city did the acrobatic
          team operate?

bavier, frances   In what television series did
                   William Bishop, James Dunn
                   and Michael O'Shea live in a
                   rooming house owned by
                   FRANCES BAVIER?

beat the clock   What company sponsored *BEAT
                  THE CLOCK?*

beau geste   Who played the three brothers in
              BEAU GESTE?

benny, jack   What were JACK BENNY's
               two theme songs?
               What was the name of the sing-
               ing group which did many of
               the commercials for Jack?
               Who is Frank Nelson?
               Where did Mary Livingston
               work?
               Who played Mr. Kitzel?
               What was Jack's parrot's name?
               Who taught her to talk?

batman	Alfred—the kindly, bald gent who dusted the Batcave and answered the Batbell
	Dick Grayson was the ward of Bruce Wayne, DC Comics's answer to Hugh Hefner
	Gotham City (not far from Metropolis)
bavier, frances	*It's a Great Life*
beat the clock	Sylvania (Do you remember the big to-do when they introduced "Halo-Light"?)
beau geste	Gary Cooper, Ray Milland, Robert Preston
benny, jack	"Love in Bloom," "Etude No. 1" (a violin exercise by Rodolphe Kreutzer)
	The Sportsmen
	He was the guy who got on Jack's nerves by showing up in many roles and saying, "Ye-e-s?"
	May's Department Store
	Art Auerbach
	Polly, educated by Dennis Day and Rochester (Eddie Anderson)

14

benson, bobby	What was the name of BOBBY BENSON's genuine palomino pony?
bergen, edgar	Who was EDGAR BERGEN's bandleader?
berle, milton	What was the name of MILTON BERLE's secretary?
beulah	For what family did BEULAH work?
	Who was her best friend?
bible	According to the song, "THE BIBLE TELLS ME SO," what's the way to live successfully?
big cheese	Who was "THE BIG CHEESE"?
bigdome, mr.	Who works for MR. BIGDOME?
big john	Who was the villain on *BIG JOHN AND SPARKY?*
	What was Big John's last name?
	On what other show did he and Sparky appear?

benson, bobby	Amigo
bergen, edgar	Ray Noble, the sophisticated British bandleader who was always being one-upped by Mortimer Snerd
berle, milton	Maxine
beulah	the Hendersons Oriole
bible	have faith, hope and charity
big cheese	Super Mouse (no relation to Mighty)
bigdome, mr.	Little Iodine's father, Henry Tremblechin
big john	Montmorency Clutchwrighter Arthur *No School Today*

16

big payoff	Who was the host of *THE BIG PAYOFF?*
big top	Who was the strong man on *THE BIG TOP?*
blackboard jungle	Who played Daddy-O in *BLACKBOARD JUNGLE?*
black pete	BLACK PETE is the arch-enemy of whom?
blondie	Who draws "BLONDIE"? What is the name of Mr. Dithers's wife?
bluster, phineas	What was the name of PHINEAS T. BLUSTER's Spanish-speaking brother?
bob, buffalo	When BUFFALO BOB went on vacation from *Howdy Doody,* who took his place as ringleader of the peanut gallery?

big payoff	Randy Merriman (Bess Myerson, the lady in mink, was his assistant.)
big top	Circus Dan the Muscle Man (Dan Lurie)
blackboard jungle	Glenn Ford was the harrassed schoolteacher.
black pete	Mickey Mouse *(q.v.)* (How could anyone want to hurt Mickey Mouse?)
blondie	Chic Young, who also draws Dagwood, Alexander and Cookie Bumstead, Mr. and Mrs. Herb Woodley, Mr. and Mrs. Dithers, Mr. Beasley, Elmo, Daisy, Elmer and a few assorted salesmen
	Cora
bluster, phineas	Don Jose
bob, buffalo	Jimmy Blaine and, occasionally, Ted Brown

bogart, humphrey

Who played HUMPHREY BO-GART's mother in *Dead End?*

In *The Big Sleep,* who played Canino, the gunman?

What song was Sam asked to play again in *Casablanca?*

boone, pat

What kind of shoes did PAT BOONE wear?

bosco

Sing the BOSCO jingle.

boston blackie

What was the name of the in-spector on *BOSTON BLACK-IE?*

Who portrayed Blackie on tele-vision?

bogart, humphrey	Marjorie Main (also famous as Pa Kettle's wife, Ma)
	Bob Steele, of range-riding fame (Bogart, of course, played Philip Marlowe.)
	"As Time Goes By," sung and played by Dooley Wilson
boone, pat	white bucks (which didn't look anything like Elvis Presley's blue suede shoes)
bosco	I love Bosco—it's rich and chocolatey. Chocolate-flavored Bosco is mighty good for me. Momma puts it in my milk for extra energy; Bosco gives me iron and sunshine vitamin D. Oh! I love Bosco—that's the drink for me.
boston blackie	Faraday
	Chester Morris, noted for patent-leather hair

box brothers   What were the first names of the
                BOX BROTHERS?

                Who portrayed them on the
                short-lived television series
                which bore their name?

boyd, jimmy   What did JIMMY BOYD want
                for Christmas?

                The following year, after he had
                gotten what he wanted, where
                did he see Mommy kissing
                Santa Claus?

boyd, william   What was the name of WIL-
                LIAM BOYD's horse?

boynton, mr.   What was the name of MR.
                BOYNTON's frog?

bradley, truman What bizarre television series was
                hosted by TRUMAN BRAD-
                LEY?

breakfast   In what city does *THE BREAK-
                FAST CLUB* originate?

box brothers	Harvey, Gilmore
	Bob Sweeney, Gale Gordon (best known for his magnificent portrayal of Our Miss Brooks's overbearing principal, Osgood Conklin—*See* brooks, our miss.)
boyd, jimmy	his two front teeth, among other things
	underneath the mistletoe
boyd, william	Topper (*See* cassidy, hopalong.)
boynton, mr.	Macdougal (not to be confused with Miss Brooks's landlady's cat—*See* brooks, our miss.)
bradley, truman	*Science Fiction Theater* (Mr. Bradley also played the radio announcer in that box-office smash movie, *The Horn Blows at Midnight.*)
breakfast	Chicago (Don MacNeil was, is, and probably always will be host.)

brewer, theresa	Where did THERESA BREWER put another nickel?
brooks, our miss	What is OUR MISS BROOKS's first name?
	Who was Miss Brooks's land-lady and what was the name of the landlady's cat?
brown, birmingham	What was BIRMINGHAM BROWN's occupation?
brown, buster	Sing the BUSTER BROWN jingle.
	What was Buster Brown's dog's name and where did he live?
bug, bucky	What was strange about the way BUCKY BUG spoke?
	With whom did Bucky live?
bunny, bugs	Who was the bearded prospector often in conflict with BUGS BUNNY?

brewer, theresa	in the nickelodeon
brooks, our miss	Constance Mrs. Davis; Minerva
brown, birmingham	chauffeur for Charlie Chan *(q.v.)*

brown, buster	I got shoes,
	You got shoes,
	Everybody's gotta have shoes.
	But there's only one kind
	   of shoes for me—
	GOOD OLD BUSTER
	   BROWN SHOES!
	
	Tige, in a shoe (with Buster)

bug, bucky	He spoke in rhyme. Now don't get mad— 'Cause for a bug That ain't too bad. his wife
bunny, bugs	Yosemite Sam (one of the finer Warner Bros. creations)

burns and allen

What was the theme song of GEORGE BURNS and GRACIE ALLEN?

Who was their announcer?

What is the first name of their stepson?

bushel and peck

What quantitative measure do you associate with BUSHEL AND A PECK and a hug around the neck?

caesar, sid

What three actresses played SID CAESAR's wife on *Show of Shows* and *Caesar's Hour?*

What song˚ did the Three Haircuts sing on *Caesar's Hour?*

calhoun, cagey

Who was CAGEY CALHOUN, the theatrical agent played by Jesse White?

calhoun, haystacks

What was HAYSTACKS CALHOUN's submission hold?

What did he wear around his neck?

burns and allen	"Love Nest"
	Harry Von Zell (not to be confused with next-door neighbor Blanche Morton's husband, Harry)
	Ronnie
bushel and peck	a barrel and a heap
caesar, sid	Imogene Coca, Nanette Fabray, Janet Blair
	"You Are So Rare to Me"
calhoun, cagey	Susan McNamara's archrival on *Private Secretary*
calhoun, haystacks	The Big Splash (Haystacks—all 601 pounds of him—fell on his opponent, or so it seemed.)
	a horseshoe on a heavy chain

camptown racetrack	How long is the CAMPTOWN RACETRACK?
canyon, steve	Who played STEVE CANYON on television?
carnation	Where did CARNATION Evaporated Milk come from?
cassidy, hopalong	Who played HOPALONG CASSIDY's sidekick in the television series?
cavendish, butch	What was the name of BUTCH CAVENDISH's gang?
chan, charlie	Name the four actors who played CHARLIE CHAN in movies and on television. Who created Chan?
chase, ilka	On what panel show did ILKA CHASE appear regularly? Who emceed that show?
chinese checkers	What is the shape of the playing surface of a CHINESE CHECKERS board?
chipmunks	Who were Walt Disney's CHIPMUNKS?

27

camptown racetrack	five miles
canyon, steve	Norman Fredericks (who also played Kasim on *Jungle Jim*)
carnation	contented cows
cassidy, hopalong	Edgar Buchanan
cavendish, butch	The Hole-in-the-Wall Gang (the gang that ambushed the Lone Ranger—*q.v.*)
chan, charlie	Warner Oland, Sidney Toler, Roland Winters, J. Carrol Naish
	Earl Derr Biggers
chase, ilka	*Masquerade Party*
	Peter Donald
chinese checkers	a six-pointed star
chipmunks	Chip and Dale, the earthbound Heckle and Jeckle

circus boy	What was the name of the circus owner on *CIRCUS BOY?*
cisco kid, the	What was the name of THE CISCO KID's horse?
	Who played Pancho on television?
clawhold	What heavyweight wrestler invented the CLAWHOLD?
	What did he do to Yukon Eric?
cody, commando	How did COMMANDO CODY get about when he was helping people in distress?
comics	What COMICS are *good* comics?
consodine, tim	Who were TIM CONSODINE and David Stolley?
cottontail, peter	Where did PETER COTTONTAIL hop?
cox, wally	Who was WALLY COX's elderly female colleague in the *Mr. Peepers* series?
crayolas	Who manufactured CRAYOLAS?

29

circus boy	Big Tim Champion (The boy was little Mickey Walker.)
cisco kid	Diablo (a pinto which was no relation to Scout) Leo Carillo
clawhold	Killer (né Walter) Kowalski He drop-kicked off part of Eric's ear
cody, commando	He flew by means of miniature jets strapped to his back
comics	"Dell Comics are *Good* Comics"
consodine, tim	Spin and Marty on *The Mickey Mouse Club* (*See* mouseketeers)
cottontail, peter	down the bunny trail (hippety-hoppety)
cox, wally	Mrs. Gurney, ably played by Marian Lorne
crayolas	Binney and Smith, Inc.

cream of wheat | What children's radio program was associated with CREAM OF WHEAT?

cry | *See* ray, johnny.

czechoslovakia | Who was the only major-league baseball player born in CZECHOSLOVAKIA?

dallas, stella | What was the name of STELLA DALLAS' daughter?

dance | What is the proper response to "DANCE WITH ME, HENRY?"

dancing | What famous DANCING couple hosted a television program? What was the name of the program?

dante's inferno | Who starred in *DANTE'S INFERNO?*

dear phoebe | What was the theme song of *DEAR PHOEBE?*

december bride | What was the cast of *DECEMBER BRIDE?*

31

cream of wheat	*Let's Pretend*
czechoslovakia	Elmer Valo, the pride and joy of the town of Ribnic
dallas, stella	Lolly (Laurel)
dance	"All right, baby."
dancing	Arthur and Kathryn Murray hosted *Arthur Murray's Dance Party*.
dante's inferno	Howard Duff, who also appeared in *Mr. Adams and Eve* with his wife, Ida Lupino
dear phoebe	"Love Is Sweeping the Country" (Peter Lawford was Phoebe.)
december bride	Spring Byington as Lilly, Frances Rafferty as Ruth, Dean Miller as Matt, Harry Morgan as Pete, Verna Felton as Hilda

32

deeds, mr.

In *MR. DEEDS GOES TO TOWN,* who played opposite Gary Cooper?

denton, walter

With whom did WALTER DENTON eat breakfast before he went to school?

derringer, yancy

Who was YANCY DERRINGER's faithful Indian companion? Who played him?

What does the Indian's name mean?

Where do they sing of Yancy Derringer?

de wilde, brandon

What was the short-lived television series in which BRANDON DE WILDE played a teen-aged boy?

diamond, don

On what two television series did DON DIAMOND regularly appear?

diamond, richard

Who played RICHARD DIAMOND on radio?

What was the name of the switchboard operator on the Diamond television series?

deeds, mr.

Jean Arthur, in the part of the cynical newspaperwoman

denton, walter

Our Miss Brooks (Eve Arden)

derringer, yancy

Pahoo Katawa, played by X. Brands (Jock Mahoney played Mr. Derringer, the New Orleans gambler.)

wolf who stand in water (i.e., wet wolf)

in manor house, on riverboat, and now and then in jail

de wilde, brandon

Jamie

diamond, don

Zorro (as the corporal) and *Kit Carson* (as Kit's sidekick)

diamond, richard

Dick Powell (David Janssen was in the television series.)

Sam, whose legs and voice were those of Mary Tyler Moore

34

ding dong
: Who was the teacher on *DING DONG SCHOOL?*

dink, winky
: Who narrated WINKY DINK's adventure stories?

: How could television viewers get Winky out of trouble?

doctor
: What was the name of DR. CHRISTIAN's nurse? Who played the role?

doggie
: Who sang "HOW MUCH IS THAT DOGGIE IN THE WINDOW?"

dollar a second
: Who sponsored *DOLLAR A SECOND?*

: How could a contestant lose all the money he had accumulated?

doody, howdy
: *See* bob, buffalo.

down
: Who was the moderator of *DOWN YOU GO?*

dracula
: What was the name of COUNT DRACULA's henchman?

ding dong	Miss Frances (Dr. Frances Horwich)
dink, winky	Jack Barry, of *Twenty-One* fame by drawing on the magic screen all true "Winky Dink and You" believers placed over their television screens
doctor	Judy Price, played by Rosemary De Camp
doggie	Patti Page
dollar a second	Mogen David wine by the occurrence of "The Outside Event"
down	Bergan Evans (He also moderated *The Last Word*.)
dracula	Renfield

dragnet | On *DRAGNET,* (*Badge 714,* as it was called in the reruns), who was Joe Friday's right-hand man? Who played the role?

What company produced the show?

How many times did the mallet strike at the end of each program?

In what county courts were the criminals tried?

droodles | Who drew DROODLES?

drummond, ace | Sing the first two lines of ACE DRUMMOND's favorite song.

duck, donald | Who was the eccentric inventor in "DONALD DUCK" comics?

How did $crooge McDuck bathe in his money?

What was Donald's original license number?

Who was Grandma Duck's hired hand?

What kind of car did Grandma drive?

37

dragnet	Frank Smith, played by Ben Alexander
	Mark VII, Ltd.
	Two
	Los Angeles County (". . . in and for the county of . . .")
droodles	bespectacled Roger Price, who must have irked many a waiter before fame came his way
drummond, ace	"Give me the open sky, Give me a ship to fly . . ."
duck, donald	Gyro Gearloose (the fellow with the lightbulb for a friend)
	He dived in it like a porpoise, except when he was protecting it from the Beagle Boys.
	313
	Gus Goose
	an electric car which must have had the longest extension cord in Duckburg

duffy   Who starred in *DUFFY'S TAV-ERN?*

duncan, archie   Name the two television series in which **ARCHIE DUNCAN** played.

durante, jimmy   Sing the song **JIMMY DU-RANTE** sang on his television shows just before he said goodnight to Mrs. Calabash, wherever she was.

dwarfs   Name the **SEVEN DWARFS.**

earp, wyatt   What group sang the **WYATT EARP** theme song?

erwin, stu   Who played Jackie on *THE STU ERWIN SHOW?* What other major role has she had on television?

duffy	Ed Gardner (as Archie, the chatty bartender)
duncan, archie	*Sherlock Holmes* (as Inspector La Strade) and *Robin Hood* (as Little John)
durante, jimmy	"Goodnight, goodnight, goodnight; It's time to say goodnight. Goodnight, goodnight, goodnight; What more is there to say but goodnight We've had a few laughs, and it's time to toodle-loo; Adios, auf Wiedersehen and Inka-dinka-doo. Goodnight, goodnight, goodnight; Goodnight, goodnight."
dwarfs	Bashful, Doc, Dopey, Grumpy, Happy, Sleepy, Sneezy
earp, wyatt	the Ken Darby Singers
erwin, stu	Sheila James; Zelda Gilroy, Dobie Gillis's would-be sweetheart

evans, dale	Name DALE EVANS' horse.
	What was the name of Roy Rogers' dog?
	What was Roy and Dale's theme song?
	What was the middle name of Roy's sidekick?
falcon, maltese	*See* spade, sam.
father knows best	Give the cast of *FATHER KNOWS BEST*.
	What were the names and nicknames of Jim and Margaret Anderson's daughters?
	What was the name of the gardener at the Anderson home in Springfield?
fisher, eddie	What did EDDIE FISHER say you should do when you're worried and can't sleep?
	How much heart did Eddie say you've gotta have?
fleer's fortune	Where could you find your FLEER'S FORTUNE?

evans, dale	Buttermilk
	Bullet
	"Happy Trails"
	(Pat) Aloysius (Brady), the only cowboy in history to kiss his jeep
father knows best	Robert Young, Jane Wyatt, Elinore Donahue, Billy Gray, Laurin Chapin
	Betty (Princess), Cathy (Kitten) (Bud was not a daughter.)
	Frank (played by Natividad Vacio)
fisher, eddie	"just count your blessings instead of sheep"
	"miles and miles and miles"
fleer's fortune	in Fleer's Double Bubble Gum

flower	Who is "THE FLOWER OF THE MUSICAL WORLD"?
fosdick, fearless	Who was FEARLESS FOS-DICK's assistant?
four-star theater	Who were the stars of *SINGER FOUR-STAR THEATER?*
foudini	*See* pinhead and foudini.
frawley, william	What couple did WILLIAM FRAWLEY and Vivian Vance portray in one of the biggest rating-getters of all time? In what other series did Frawley appear regularly?
frosty	How was FROSTY THE SNOW-MAN's face made?
fudd, elmer	What color are ELMER FUDD's shoes?
gander, gladstone	Who was GLADSTONE GAN-DER?
gang busters	Who created *GANG BUSTERS?*

43

flower	Ray Bloch, who used to lead traveling music for Jackie Gleason
fosdick, fearless	Shmoozer was Fosdick's kemosabe.
four-star theater	David Niven, Charles Boyer, Ida Lupino, Dick Powell
frawley, william	Fred and Ethel Mertz, the Ricardos' neighbors on *I Love Lucy* (the first of the Desilu productions)
	My Three Sons, which starred Fred MacMurray
frosty	with a corncob pipe and a button nose and two eyes made out of coal
fudd, elmer	red (except on covers, where they are usually brown)
gander, gladstone	$crooge McDuck's annoyingly lucky nephew (*See* duck, donald.)
gang busters	Philips H. Lords

get a job
What were the ridiculous lyrics to the chorus of *"GET A JOB"*?

ghostriders
Who sang "GHOSTRIDERS IN THE SKY"?

gildersleeve
Who were the two actors who portrayed THE GREAT GILDERSLEEVE?

gillette
What was the name of the GILLETTE parrot?

gillis, dobie
What was DOBIE GILLIS' carefree friend Maynard's last name?

Who played Dobie's mother and father?

gillis, jim
See riley, chester.

gleason, jackie
What was the name of the obnoxious millionaire JACKIE GLEASON portrayed?

What was the name of Ed Norton's wife in *The Honeymooners?* Who played her?

45

get a job	"Sha da da da, sha da da da da . . .
	Well, yip yip yip yip yip yip yip yip,
	Boom boom boom boom boom— Get a job."
ghostriders	Vaughn Monroe, whose voice was like a foghorn in a heavy mist
gildersleeve	Harold Peary, Willard Waterman
gillette	Sharpie
gillis, dobie	Krebs (another great Max Shulman name)
	Florida Friebus and Frank Faylen
gleason, jackie	Reggie van Gleason III, the antithesis of the Chaplinesque Poor Soul
	Trixie, played by Joyce Randolph (Ed Norton, played by Art Carney, was bus-driver Ralph Kramden's upstairs neighbor —the guy who worked in a sewer.)

gobel, george	Who played GEORGE GOBEL's wife?
	Who led the orchestra on George's show?
	Who was the vocalist?
godfrey, arthur	Whom did ARTHUR GODFREY fire?
goldberg, molly	What were the names of MOLLY GOLDBERG's husband, uncle, son, and daughter?
	What was the name of the uncle's son? What was the son's profession?
gorcey, leo	What did LEO GORCEY have in common with Billy Hallop?
gordon, commissioner	On whom did COMMISSIONER GORDON rely for help?
gordon, flash	Who played Ming the Merciless in the FLASH GORDON serials?
	How was the city of Vulcan kept suspended in space before Dr. Zarkov's revolutionary invention?

gobel, george	Jeff Donnell
	John Scott Trotter
	pretty, perky Peggy King
godfrey, arthur	the Mariners, Frank Parker, Marian Marlowe and Julius LaRosa (About the only one he didn't fire was Haleloke.)
goldberg, molly	Jake, David, Sammy, and Rosalie
	Solly, the doctor (of course)
gorcey, leo	Leo succeeded Billy as leader of the Dead End Kids (the Bowery Boys)
gordon, commissioner	Batman and Robin, whom he called by flashing the Batsignal
gordon, flash	Charles Middleton
	by energy supplied by an atomic furnace stoked by slaves of the Vulcan king

graham, billy	Who is BILLY GRAHAM's associate evangelist?
graham brothers	What were the first names of the famous tag-team combination, the GRAHAM BROTHERS?
graham, otto	Who was Cleveland quarterback OTTO GRAHAM's successor, whose performance convinced Graham to come back out of retirement?
grauer, ben	BEN GRAUER was associated with what musical broadcasts?
green arrow	What was GREEN ARROW's identity?
green hornet	Who was the GREEN HORNET's valet, the only person who knew his secret identity?
	What was the Hornet's theme song?
grundy, miss	Who is MISS GRUNDY?
gunn, peter	What night spot did PETER GUNN habituate?

graham, billy	Grady Wilson
graham brothers	Jerry and Eddie
graham, otto	George Ratterman
grauer, ben	Arturo Toscanini's concerts with the NBC Symphony
green arrow	Oliver Queen, whose sidekick, Roy Harper, was known and loved as Speedy
green hornet	Cato, the Japanese, who became a Filipino on December 7, 1941
	"Flight of the Bumblebee"
grundy, miss	the teacher in "Archie" comics
gunn, peter	Mother's (where Edie Hart, Peter's girl, sang)

gunsmoke On *GUNSMOKE,* what were the last names of Chester, Doc, and Kitty?

In the radio version, what effect did Matt Dillon say being a marshal has?

haley, bill How long did BILL HALEY AND THE COMETS plan to rock, rock, rock?

hansen, lars Where (street and city) did LARS HANSEN and family live?

hardy boys Name THE HARDY BOYS and their father.

Who were the boys' girlfriends?

hardy, andy Who portrayed ANDY HARDY's father in the MGM movie series?

heartbreak hotel *See* presley, elvis.

heartline With whom do you associate *THE HEARTLINE?*

heartline, mary Who was MARY HEARTLINE?

gunsmoke   Goode, Adams, Russell

"It makes a man watchful and a little bit lonely."

haley, bill   till broad daylight

hansen, lars   Steiner Street, San Francisco *(See "I remember mama")*

hardy boys   Frank and Joe, Fenton (the detective)

Callie Shaw fell for Frank, and Iola Morton jumped for Joe.

hardy, andy   Lewis Stone played the wise judge who advised Andy through those troublesome years.

heartline   Warren Hull, emcee of *Strike It Rich*

heartline, mary   the majorette on *Super Circus*

hellmann's mayonnaise	What went into **HELLMANN'S REAL MAYONNAISE?**
henry	Who created *HENRY?*
hickok, wild bill	Who was **WILD BILL HICK-OK's** sidekick? Who played him on radio and television?
	Who sponsored Wild Bill's radio and television shows?
high noon	Who sang the title song in *HIGH NOON?*
	Who played Gary Cooper's wife?
hitchcock, alfred	What were **ALFRED HITCHCOCK's** first words on his television show?
	What was the theme music of his program?
	What was the most memorable adventure experienced by Cary Grant and Eva Marie Saint in the movie, *North By Northwest?*

hellmann's mayonnaise	the whole egg
henry	Carl Anderson
hickok, wild bill	Jingles; Andy Devine in both media (Guy Madison was Wild Bill.)
	Kellogg's Sugar Pops
high noon	Tex Ritter, the singing cowboy
	Grace Kelly
hitchcock, alfred	"Good evening."
	"Funeral March of the Marionettes"
	They were chased through the sculpture work of Mount Rushmore. (If you know the name of the sculptor, we don't particularly care—you're playing Minutiae.)

hit parade | Name the original cast and conductor of *YOUR HIT PARADE* on television.

Sing the show's closing theme.

holmes, sherlock | Who played **SHERLOCK HOLMES** and Dr. Watson in the movie and on television?

What was Sherl's home address?

honeymooners, the | *See* gleason, jackie.

hook, captain | *See* pan, peter.

hornblower, clarabelle | Who was **CLARABELLE HORNBLOWER**?

hound dog | *See* presley, elvis.

hug around neck | *See* bushel and peck.

hunchback | *See* quasimodo.

hit parade	Gisele MacKenzie, Dorothy Collins, Snooky Lanson, Russell Arms, Raymond Scott
	"So long for a while. That's all the songs for a while. So long to Your Hit Parade And the tunes that you picked to be played. So long."
holmes, sherlock	Basil Rathbone and Nigel Bruce in the movies; Ronald Howard and H. Marion Crawford on television
	227-B Baker Street, London (John Watson lived there, too, until he married; then he moved. Elementary.)
hornblower, clarabelle	the only woman who knew the identity of the Lone Ranger *(q.v.)* (She was *not* a clown who squirted seltzer at Princess Summerfall Winterspring.)

i married joan

What was Joan Davis's television husband's name?

Who sang "I MARRIED JOAN"?

Sing it yourself.

in the still of the night

In the rock 'n' roll song, "IN THE STILL OF THE NIGHT," when did the stars shine bright above?

i.q., dr.

What did you have to do in the game called DR. I.Q. JUMP (Yogo)?

i married joan | Judge Bradley J. Stevens (played by Jim Backus, the voice of Mr. Magoo)

the Roger Wagner Chorale

"I married Joan—what a girl, what a whirl, what a life!
Oh, I married Joan—love is blind, what a mind, what a wife!
Giddy and gay, although she keeps my heart laughing,
Never know where her brain has flown.
To each his own: can't deny that's why I married Joan.

in the still of the night | that night in May

i.q., dr. | remove all the pegs from the playing board until only one remained, in the center

i remember mama	From what book was the television show, *I REMEMBER MAMA* (starring Peggy Wood) adapted? Who was the author?
	Name Mama's husband, children, niece, and nephew
irma	*See* my friend irma.
it could be you	Who emceed *IT COULD BE YOU?*
i've got a loverly bunch of coconuts	In the Song "I'VE GOT A LOVERLY BUNCH OF CO-CONUTS," how much does rolling or bowling cost?
jane	*See* tarzan.
jeff	*See* mutt.
joker, the	Whose enemy was THE JOK-ER?
jonathan, don leo	What was DON LEO JONA-THAN's profession?

i remember mama	*Mama's Bank Account* by Kathryn Forbes husband Lars (an industrious carpenter), son Nels (who wanted to be a doctor), elder daughter Kathryn (who wrote the book), younger daughter Dagmar (played by Robin Morgan), niece Ingeborg (*see* bad seed, the), nephew Theodore Roosevelt Ryan (who was called T.R. by everyone, even Aunt Jenny—pronounce that "Yenny"—and Aunt Trina)
it could be you	Bill Leyden, who seemed to enjoy reuniting contestants with long-lost relatives
i've got a loverly bunch of coconuts	a penny a pitch
joker, the	Batman's
jonathan, don leo	wrestler (all 6'7" of him)

jukebox jury | Who was the emcee of *JUKE-BOX JURY?*

jungle jim | What was the name of the ape on *JUNGLE JIM?*

junior miss | Who played Fuffy Adams in *JUNIOR MISS?*

jupiter, johnny | What were the names of the two robots on *JOHNNY JUPITER?*

kat, krazy | Who was the mouse in *KRAZY KAT?*

katzenjammer kids | Name the KATZENJAMMER KIDS.

kaye, danny | How did DANNY KAYE describe the king's new clothes?

kazootie, rootie | Who was ROOTIE KAZOOTIE's archenemy?

What did he steal from Rootie's girlfriend, Polka Dottie?

What was the name of Rootie's dog?

61

jukebox jury	Peter Potter, whose show was first a hit and then a miss
jungle jim	Tamba
junior miss	Beverly Wills (Joan Davis's real daughter, by the way)
jupiter, johnny	Reject and Major Domo
kat, krazy	Ignatz, one of George Herriman's brilliant characters who populated Coconino County
katzenjammer kids	Hans, a Teutonic Dennis the Menace, and Fritz, a male version of Little Iodine (Ach! Himmel!)
kaye, danny	"The king's new clothes are altogether, but altogether, but altogether the most remarkable suit of clothes that I have ever seen."
kazootie, rooty	Poison Sumac
	her dots
	Galapoochie

keen, mr.   What, exactly, was MR. KEEN's
                   profession?

king, sky   What was the name of SKY
                   KING's plane?

kingfish   *See* amos 'n' andy.

kitzel, mr.   *See* benny, jack.

knock   KNOCK, KNOCK.

kong, king   With whom did KING KONG
                   fall in love?

kookie   Who played KOOKIE on *77 Sun-
                   set Strip?*

kovacs, ernie   What were the names of the poet
                   and the magician created by
                   ERNIE KOVACS?

                   What was his musical aggrega-
                   tion?

kukla, fran and   Who is the veteran puppeteer of
ollie   *KUKLA, FRAN AND OL-
                   LIE?*

                   What was the name of the Kukla-
                   politans' neighborhood witch?

keen, mr.	tracer of lost persons
king, sky	Songbird
knock	Who's there?
kong, king	Fay Wray
kookie	Edd Byrnes, the parking-lot attendant with the comb
kovacs, ernie	Percy Dovetonsils; Matzoh Hepplewhite; the Nairobi Trio
kukla, fran and	Burr Tillstrom
ollie	Beulah

lane, lois	Who played LOIS LANE on television?
la rue, lash	Who was LASH LA RUE's sidekick?
lassie	Who played the members of LASSIE's original television family?
latin	Complete the following poem: LATIN is a dead language, as dead as dead can be. . . .
lee, pinky	How did PINKY LEE say you could recognize him?
life with luigi	Who played Pasquali in *LIFE WITH LUIGI?*
line-up	Who were the co-stars of *THE LINE-UP?*
little, chicken	Who ate CHICKEN LITTLE?

lane, lois	Noel Neill and Phyllis Coates played Superman's dauntless damsel
la rue, lash	Al "Fuzzy" St. John, who, in his spare time, was the sidekick of Larry "Buster" Crabbe
lassie	Tommy Rettig, Jan Clayton, George Cleveland (When Tommy outgrew his role, Lassie got a new family—John Provost, June Lockhart, John Sheppod and George Chandler.)
latin	. . . Once it killed the Romans and now it's killing me.
lee, pinky	by his checkered hat and checkered coat, the funny giggle in his throat
life with luigi	Salvatore Baccalone
line-up	Warner Anderson and Tom Tully pounded their San Francisco beat.
little, chicken	Foxy Loxy, who knew what he wanted and went after it

little lulu

Who is the speedy character in the prose stories in "LITTLE LULU" comics?

With whom does Lulu babysit? Who is Iggy?

Why didn't Lulu and Annie join the club formed by Tubby and his friends?

lone ranger, the

Who played THE LONE RANGER on radio and on television?

Who was Fred Foy?

Who created the masked rider of the plains?

Where did the radio show originate?

Everyone knows Jay Silverheels played Tonto on television. Who played on radio the faithful Indian companion who rode Scout?

Recite the introduction to *The Lone Ranger,* beginning: "With his faithful Indian companion, Tonto, . . ."

little lulu	Knot-knee
	Alvin
	the bald, younger brother of Annie, Lulu's best friend
	because the boys had placed a big sign on the clubhouse, reading "NO GIRLS ALLOWED"
lone ranger, the	Brace Beamer on radio, John Hart and Clayton Moore on television
	your announcer
	George W. Trendle
	WXYZ in Detroit
	John Todd (who was not an Indian)
	". . . the daring and resourceful masked rider of the plains led the fight for law and order in the early western United States. Nowhere in the pages of history can one find a greater champion of justice. Return with us now to those thrilling days of yesteryear. From out of the past come the thundering hoofbeats of the great horse Silver. The Lone Ranger rides again. . . ."

love	Who sang the title song in the movie, *LOVE ME OR LEAVE ME?*
lucky strike	How do you show how firmly packed a LUCKY STRIKE is?
lux video theater	How did *LUX VIDEO THEATER* open?
lydia	Who sang "LYDIA, THE TATTOOED LADY"?
mad	Who was the first editor of *MAD?*
mambo italiano	Who recorded the hit version of "MAMBO ITALIANO"?
manchu, fu	Who played FU MANCHU in the movie series?
marge	Who is the witch created by MARGE?

love	Doris Day, who played Ruth Etting, the torch singer managed by a limping James Cagney
lucky strike	You tear a strip the length of the cigarette and remove the paper. Then you hold up the round, firm and fully packed glob of tobacco, smile and say, "L.S./M.F.T.—Lucky Strike Means Fine Tobacco."
lux video theater	with searchlights scanning the sky
lydia	Groucho Marx in *A Day at the Circus*
mad	Harvey Kurtzman
mambo italiano	Rosemary Clooney
manchu, fu	Boris Karloff
marge	Witch Hazel, the bane of Little Lulu's existence

marvel, captain

Where did CAPTAIN MARVEL get his lightening bolts?

What does *Shazam* stand for?

Who was Captain Marvel's arch-rival?

marx, groucho

Whose money was GROUCHO MARX (alias Hugo Quacken-bush, alias Wolf J. Flywheel) usually after in the movies?

Who announced for Groucho on *You Bet Your Life?*

Who was the custodian of The Secret Word?

mary jane

How did MARY JANE become small?

massey, curt

Who blended her voice with CURT MASSEY's on a daily radio program from the west coast?

maverick, brett

Who is BRETT MAVERICK's companion? What is his game?

marvel, captain

He said "Shazam!" and the wizard threw them to him from the Rock of Eternity

Solomon, Hercules, Atlas, Zeus, Achilles, Mercury

Dr. Savannah (a cruel Yul)

marx, groucho

Margaret Dumont's

George Fenneman

a duck with a marked resemblance to Groucho

mary jane

She closed her eyes, crossed her fingers and said:

"Now I shut my eyes real tight
And then I wish with all my might:
Magic words of poof poof piffles—
Make me just as small as Sniffles."

massey, curt

Martha Tilton, whose recording of "Bei Mir Bist Du Schoen" challenged that of the Andrews Sisters

maverick, brett

Luck is his companion; gambling is his game.

maynard, ken	With whom did KEN MAY-NARD ride?
	What was the name of Ken's horse?
maypo	What was the name of the little boy who wanted his MAYPO?
ncduck, $crooge	*See* duck, donald.
mcgee, fibber	Where did FIBBER McGEE and MOLLY live?
mcgillicuddy, lucille	Who is LUCILLE McGILLI-CUDDY?
michaels, pat	What children's show was hosted by the imaginative PAT MI-CHAELS?
milland, ray	RAY MILLAND starred in two television shows. Name them.
midnight	What did MIDNIGHT THE CAT say?
mind reading	Who was the only performer in history to fool a network into giving him a MIND-READ-ING show?

73

maynard, ken	Hoot Gibson and Bob Steele Tarzan
maypo	Markie
mcgee, fibber	77 Wistful Vista
mcgillicuddy, lucille	Lucy Ricardo (Lucille Ball), be- fore she was married to Ricky (Desi Arnaz) (*See* i love lucy.)
michaels, pat	*The Magic Cottage* (the home of more imaginary characters than Never Never Land)
milland, ray	*Meet Mr. McNulty* (in which he played a mild-mannered pro- fessor at a girls' college) and *Markham* (in which he played a Peter Gunn with ruffles)
midnight	ni-ice
mind reading	The Great Dunninger

ming the merciless	*See* gordon, flash.
minoso, minnie	What was MINNIE MINOSO's real first name?
monkey	What did the MONKEY say to the chimp?
	Who married the monkey and the chimp and when did he do it?
monopoly	What is the only Community Chest card which gives you ten dollars in "MONOPOLY?"
moore, garry	Sing the line the cast of *THE GARRY MOORE SHOW* sang at the end of each program, following "That Wonderful Year" presentation.
moron	What did the MORON throw out the window?
morton, blanche	Who played BLANCHE MORTON?
mountain, big rock candy	What kind of trees and fountains can be found on the BIG ROCK CANDY MOUNTAIN?

75

minoso, minnie	Orestes (Minnie, of course, was the fine leftfielder of the Chicago White Sox.)
monkey	"Abba-dabba-dabba-dabba-dabba-dabba-dabba" the big baboon one night in June
monopoly	"You have won second prize in a beauty contest."
moore, garry	"Do you recall, or remember at all, that wonderful, wonderful year?"
moron	the clock (If you don't know why, ask someone.)
morton, blanche	Bea Benadaret, who, with her husband Harry (Larry Keating), suffered through the post-vaudeville pranks of Burns and Allen
mountain, big rock candy	cigarette trees and soda water fountains

mouse, mickey	Name MICKEY MOUSE's nephews.
mouseketeers	Why did the MOUSEKETEERS say they would see you real soon?
mule, talking	Who was the voice of FRANCIS THE TALKING MULE? Who was Fran's leading man?
mummy	What kept THE MUMMY active? (No, it wasn't the daddy!)
mutt and jeff	In the comic strip, *MUTT AND JEFF,* what is the name of Jeff's twin?
my friend irma	Who played Irma on *MY FRIEND IRMA?*
my little margie	What did MY LITTLE MARGIE (Gale Storm) say whenever it was discovered that she had done something wrong? What did her father, Vern Albright (Charles Farrell), say at the end of each show? For whom did Margie's father work? Who was his girlfriend? Who played Mrs. Odets?

mouse, mickey	Morty and Ferdy
mouseketeers	Why? Because they liked you!
mule, talking	Chill Wills Donald O'Connor
mummy	a nectar made from crushed tanna leaves (tasted a little like chicken soup)
mutt and jeff	Julius, who also likes to sit on curbs
my friend irma	Marie Wilson
my little margie	She trilled. "Well (heh, heh)—that's my little Margie." Honeywell and Todd Roberta (played by Hillary Brooke) Verne Felton on radio and Gertrude Hoffman on television

nadler, teddy	Who is TEDDY NADLER?
name's the same	Who was the emcee of *THE NAME'S THE SAME?*
name that tune	What were the contestants on *NAME THAT TUNE* required to do before they answered questions posed by George De Witt (and his predecessor, Red Benson)?
nancy	What was the name of the rich kid who always annoyed NANCY and SLUGGO?
naughty lady	How old was THE NAUGHTY LADY OF SHADY LANE?
nemo, captain	Who played CAPTAIN NEMO in *Twenty Thousand Leagues Under the Sea?*
north, pam and jerry	Who played PAM and JERRY NORTH on television?
notary sojac	In what comic strip do the words "NOTARY SOJAC" appear?

79

nadler, teddy	the general knowledge expert on *The $64,000 Question* and *The $64,000 Challenge.*
name's the same	Robert Q. Lewis
name that tune	run across the stage and ring a bell ahead of their opponents
nancy	Rollo (Butch isn't rich, and besides, he wouldn't beat up a girl.)
naughty lady	only six months
nemo, captain	James Mason
north, pam and jerry	Barbara Britten and Richard Denning
notary sojac	*Smokey Stover*

o'brien, cubby	Who was CUBBY O'BRIEN?
og, grandma	Who created GRANDMA OG?
ohm, prof.	In what comic book did PROF. OHM and The Claw appear?
old gold	Describe the OLD GOLD DANCERS.
omnibus	Who was the host on OMNIBUS?
one man's family	Who created *ONE MAN'S FAMILY?*
	What was the name of the ever expanding brood?
our gal sunday	What question did the story of *OUR GAL SUNDAY* ask?
our gang	What was the great delusion of Alfalfa Schweitzer of OUR GANG?
out of the inkwell	Who drew the *OUT OF THE INKWELL* series which featured Koko the Clown?

o'brien, cubby — a little boy who was paid an awful lot of money for wearing mouse's ears on *The Mickey Mouse Club*

og, grandma — Cliff Arquette (Charlie Weaver), who also created Elsie Crack, Leonard Box, and the other rustic inhabitants of Mt. Idy

ohm, prof. — *Mighty Mouse*

old gold — two girls with cigarette-pack costumes and white boots

omnibus — Alistair Cooke

one man's family — Carleton E. Morse
Barber

our gal sunday — "Can a young girl from a little mining town in the west find happiness as the wife of a wealthy and titled Englishman?"

our gang — that he could sing

out of the inkwell — "uncle" Max Fleischer

82

ozzie and harriet — Who played the next-door neighbor on *OZZIE AND HARRIET?* What did the Nelsons call him?

What was Harriet's maiden name?

pain, peter — Who was PETER PAIN?

paladin — What hotel did PALADIN call home?

What was his first name?

Who sang the Paladin theme song?

palooka, joe — Who created JOE PALOOKA?

pan, peter — Who were the three children in *PETER PAN?*

What was the name of their dog?

Who played Captain Hook in the oft-repeated Mary Martin television production?

pancho — *See* cisco kid.

ozzie and harriet	Don Defore, Thorny Hilliard
pain, peter	the green troll in Ben-Gay ads
paladin	the Hotel Carleton, San Francisco
	Wire (Remember his card? It said, "Have gun, will travel. Wire Paladin, San Francisco.")
	Johnny Western
palooka, joe	Ham Fisher
pan, peter	Wendy, Michael and John
	Nana
	Cyril Ritchard

pantomime quiz	Who emceed *PANTOMINE QUIZ?*
pawn shop	Where was the PAWN SHOP ON THE CORNER?
people's choice	What was the name of Jackie Cooper's dog on *THE PEOPLE'S CHOICE?*
	What was Councilman Miller's first name?
perkins, ma	What were the names of MA PERKINS' daughters?
peter and the wolf	What instruments are associated with each character in *PETER AND THE WOLF?*
philbrick, herbert	Who was HERBERT PHILBRICK?
	Who was the fink's number one contact? Who played him?
philip morris	What did Johnny do for PHILIP MORRIS?
pig, porky	What was the name of PORKY PIG's nephew?

pantomime quiz	Mike Stokey
pawn shop	in Pittsburgh, Pa.
people's choice	Cleo (a basset hound)
	Socrates (or Soc, as he was called by his girlfriend, Mandy Peoples)
perkins, ma	Fay and Ethel
peter and the wolf	Peter: string section
	bird: flute
	duck: oboe
	cat: bass clarinet
	grandfather: bassoon
	wolf: three French horns
	hunters: timpani and bass drum
philbrick, herbert	the FBI counterspy who led three lives, all of them played by Richard Carlson on television
	Jerry Gessler (played by John Zaremba)
philip morris	call
pig, porky	Cicero

86

pillsbury	How many eggs go into PILLS-BURY CAKE MIXES?
pinhead and foudini	On what television show did the puppets PINHEAD AND FOUDINI appear?
pinocchio	What was PINOCCHIO's father's name?
planet, daily	Who is the editor of *THE DAILY PLANET?*
plastic man	Who was PLASTIC MAN's sidekick?
popeye	What is the official name of the comic strip which features POPEYE and company?
praskins, violet	Who was VIOLET PRASKINS?
presley	Why ain't the hound dog a friend of ELVIS PRESLEY?
	On what street was Heartbreak Hotel?
	What was the Pelvis' first movie?
preston, sergeant	What was the name of SER-GEANT PRESTON's horse?

pillsbury	There are 13, and every once in a while, Arthur Godfrey *(q.v.)* used to break 'em and throw 'em in a bowl—when he wasn't buzzing houses with his airplane.
pinhead and foudini	*Lucky Pup*
pinocchio	Geppetto
planet, daily	Perry White
plastic man	Woozie Winks
popeye	*Thimble Theater*
praskins, violet	the switchboard operator on *Private Secretary* (played by Ann Tyrrell)
presley	He ain't never caught a rabbit. Lonely Street *Love Me Tender*
preston, sergeant	Rex

princemetal	Who played ALFRED PRINCE-METAL?
private secretary	What was Ann Sothern's middle name on *PRIVATE SECRETARY?* Who was her boss?
quaker puffed cereals	What did Gabby Hayes say was the beauty of QUAKER PUFFED WHEAT and QUAKER PUFFED RICE?
quasimodo	What three actors have played QUASIMODO in *The Hunchback of Notre Dame?*
rabbit, br'er	Where did BR'ER RABBIT not want to be throwed?
rabbit, crusader	Where was CRUSADER RABBIT's home town? Who was Crusader's sidekick?
rabbit, peter	Into whose hole did PETER RABBIT run?

princemetal — Marvin Kaplan, in *Meet Millie* (Elena Verdugo was Millie Bronson.)

private secretary — Camille (Susan C. McNamara)

Mr. Sands (played by Don Porter)

quaker puffed cereals — "You can shweeten them with shugar to shuit yourshelf," he shaid.

quasimodo — Lon Chaney, Sr. (in the silent version), Charles Laughton, and Anthony Quinn

rabbit, br'er — in da briar patch

rabbit, crusader — Galahad Glen

Rags the Tiger

rabbit, peter — Farmer MacGregor's

rags to riches   "RAGS TO RICHES" was a song popularized by_____?

railroad   How long have I been working on the RAILROAD and why?

ramar   Who played RAMAR OF THE JUNGLE?

Who sponsored the show?

ray, johnny   When did JOHNNY RAY think you should let your hair down and cry?

Here's the situation: You're walking your baby back home and you stop for a while, she gives you a smile, and puts her head on your chest. What happens next?

reid, dan   What was the name of DAN REID's horse?

reindeer   *See* claus, santa.

remley, frank   Who was FRANK REMLEY?

rags to riches   Tony Bennett

railroad   all the livelong day, just to pass the time away

ramar   Jon Hall
Good and Plenty

ray, johnny   when your sweetheart sends a letter of good-bye

She gets her powder all over your vest.

reid, dan   Victor (Dan Reid is the Lone Ranger's nephew—His father, Dan, Sr., was one of the Texas Rangers ambushed by the Butch Cavendish Gang—*q.v.*)

remley, frank   Jack Benny's drummer, noted as much for hitting the bottle as for pounding the skins

riley, chester

Where did **CHESTER A. RILEY** live?

For what company did Riley work?

Who played Otto Schmidlap, Riley's brawny but brainless co-worker?

What was the name of Riley's meek neighbor, played by Sterling Holloway?

Jim and Honeybee Gillis' son's name was —————?

rin tin tin

Who was the boy on the *RIN TIN TIN* television series?

Who was R.T.T.'s owner and trainer?

ritz, fritzie

Who was **FRITZIE RITZ's** boyfriend?

rivia-tay

Translate the following: RIVIA-TAY iz-ay appiness-hay.

robin

See batman.

robin hood

Who played **ROBIN HOOD** in the Walt Disney production?

riley, chester	1313 Blueview Terrace
	Cunningham Aircraft (He was a riveter, remember?)
	Henry "Bomber" Kulky, who later played Max Brodsky, the petty officer in *Hennessey*
	Waldo Binney
	Egbert
rin tin tin	Rusty, played by Lee Akers
	Lee Duncan
ritz, fritzie	Phil, the redhead
rivia-tay	"Trivia is happiness." (Pig Latin)
robin hood	Richard Todd (Richard Greene was the Robin Hood of the television series, and the eternally brave Errol Flynn also portrayed the legendary hero on film.)

rockwell, robert	Name two television series which featured ROBERT ROCK-WELL.
rogers, roy	*See* evans, dale.
saint, the	Name the three actors who played THE SAINT in the movies.
scared stiff	Who were the stars of the movie, *SCARED STIFF?*
scarf, long	Who wore a LONG SCARF which fell down to the floor when he opened his overcoat?
scheiman, martin j.	Who is MARTIN J. SCHEI-MAN, ESQ.?
schmidlap, otto	*See* riley, chester.
science fiction	Name two weird SCIENCE-FIC-TION comic books with "strange" as the first word of the title.
scrabble	How many blank tiles in SCRAB-BLE and what could you do with them?

rockwell, robert	*Our Miss Brooks* and *Man from Blackhawk*
saint, the	Hugh Sinclair, George Sanders, Louis Hayward
scared stiff	Dean Martin and Jerry Lewis
scarf, long	Red Buttons (ho-ho)
scheiman, martin j.	the libel lawyer for *Mad*
science fiction	*Strange Tales, Strange Adventures*
scrabble	two; use them for any letter you want, but with no point value (no double letter, double word . . .)

seuss, dr.	Who was the boy with 500 hats in the DR. SEUSS story?
shadow, the	What was THE SHADOW's identity?
	Recite the Shadow's two best-known lines.
	Who was his lovely friend and companion?
	What was the name of the police commissioner?
shmoo	Who created the SHMOO?
shoemaker's shop	What kind of shoes were in THE SHOEMAKER'S SHOP?
shore, dinah	Who co-starred with DINAH SHORE on a 15-minute radio show?
shorts, short	Who wears SHORT SHORTS?
shrimp boats	Who sang "SHRIMP BOATS"?
silent service	SILENT SERVICE was a program about _____.
silver eagle	What great radio voice portrayed THE SILVER EAGLE?

97

seuss, dr.	Bartholomew Cubbins
shadow	Lamont Cranston
	"Who knows what evil lurks in the hearts of men? The Shadow knows. (Ha, ha, ha . . .)" "The weed of crime bears bitter fruit. Crime does not pay. The Shadow knows. (Ha, ha, ha. . .)"
	Margo Lane
	Commissioner Westin
shmoo	Al Capp
shoemaker's shop	shoes to set my feet a-dancing
shore, dinah	Jack Smith (Art Baker's replacement on *You Asked For It*)
shorts, short	we
shrimp boats	Jo Stafford
silent service	submarine warfare
silver eagle	Jim Ameche

silver, long john   What was the name of LONG
                     JOHN SILVER's parrot?

silvers, phil   What was the original name of
                     PHIL SILVERS' army show?

                     Who created that military situa-
                     tion comedy?

sixteen tons   When you load SIXTEEN
                     TONS, what do you get?

sixty-four   What bank held the questions on
thousand dollar   *THE $64,000 QUESTION?*
question
                     On that ill-fated program, what
                     categories were chosen by Dr.
                     Joyce Brothers, Gino Prato
                     and Captain Richard Mc-
                     Kutcheon?

sluggo   *See* nancy.

smith, kate   Who was KATE SMITH's man-
                     ager and sidekick?

smith, nailand   Who was NAILAND SMITH?

spade, sam   Who played SAM SPADE's sec-
                     retary in *The Maltese Falcon?*

silver, long john	Captain Kidd
silvers, phil	*You'll Never Get Rich* Nat Hiken, also creator of *Car 54, Where Are You?*
sixteen tons	another day older and deeper in debt (damn tired, too)
sixty-four thousand dollar question	Manufacturer's Trust (since merged) boxing, opera, cooking (Hal March, of course, guided the treasure-hunters through peaceful plateaus and not-so-isolated isolation booths.)
smith, kate	Ted Collins
smith, nailand	Fu Manchu's archpursuer
spade, sam	Lee Patrick (who later appeared on television as Cosmo Topper's wife, Henrietta)

spring	What was the name of the SPRING that could walk up and down stairs?
stop the music	The emcee of *STOP THE MUSIC* was ——————.
straight arrow	To what tribe did STRAIGHT ARROW belong?
sullivan, ed	What was the original name of *THE ED SULLIVAN SHOW?*
super circus	Who was the ringmaster on *SUPER CIRCUS?*
superboy	Give the last name and occupation of SUPERBOY's foster parents. Who were Superboy's Kryptonic parents?
superman	Who is SUPERMAN's enemy from the fifth dimension? Who played Superman on radio?

spring	Slinky
stop the music	Bert Parks (the original "Look, Ma! No cavities!" man)
straight arrow	Comanche
sullivan, ed	*Toast of the Town*
super circus	Claude Kirschner (not to be confused with Jack Sterling, his counterpart on the Sealtest *Big Top*)
superboy	Kent, grocers
	courageous Jor-El and the lovely Lara
superman	Mr. Mxyzptlk, who could be sent back home only by being tricked into saying his name backwards (One would think that anyone who could pronounce "Kltpzyxm" should be permitted to stay.)
	Bud Collyer (also associated with *Break the Bank* and *Beat the Clock*)

talbot, lawrence	Who was LAWRENCE TAL-BOT?
tarzan	What was TARZAN's real name?
	Who was the first actor to portray Tarzan in the movies?
	What was Jane's home town?
teddy bears' picnic	At what time do the TEDDY BEARS go home to bed after their PICNIC, and why?
texaco	Sing the TEXACO jingle from *The Milton Berle Show.*
that's my boy	Who was Eddie Mayhoff's son in *THAT'S MY BOY?*
thin man, the	Who played THE THIN MAN and his wife in the movies?
	What was their dog's name?
thing	Who sang "THE THING"?
	In the song, what did everybody tell the Thing's owner to do?

talbot, lawrence	the Wolfman, played by Lon Chaney, Jr.
tarzan	Lord Greystoke
	Elmo Lincoln
	Baltimore (Her father, you remember, was a professor.)
teddy bears' picnic	at six o'clock; because they're tired little teddy bears
texaco	Oh, we're the men from Texaco, We work from Maine to Mexico, We love our job in servicing your car. We might be Texaco men, But tonight we're really showmen. As proudly we present to you . . . "The Milton Berle Show."
that's my boy	Gil Stratton, Jr.
thin man, the	William Powell as Nick Charles and Myrna Loy as Nora
	Asta
thing	Phil Harris
	"Get out of here."

third man, the	Who starred in *THE THIRD MAN?*
thomas, danny	What was the original name of *THE DANNY THOMAS SHOW?*
	Who played Danny's eldest daughter?
thomas, lowell	Who was LOWELL THOMAS' announcer?
three-d	What was the first 3-D film?
three mesquiteers	Which of the THREE MESQUITEERS was a ventriloquist?
thumbelina	When THUMBELINA's heart is full of love, how tall is she?
tipton, john	What was JOHN BERESFORD TIPTON's estate?
tock	What went TOCK-TICK-TOCK?
todd-ao	What was the first movie made in TODD-AO?
tombstone territory	What newspaper supplied most of the material for the *TOMBSTONE TERRITORY* series?

third man	Joseph Cotten, Orson Wells, Alida Valli
thomas, danny	*Make Room for Daddy* Sherry Jackson
thomas, lowell	Nelson Case
three-d	*House of Wax* (Those glasses *were* uncomfortable, weren't they?)
three mesquiteers	Max Terhune
thumbelina	nine feet
tipton, john	Silverstone (which certainly looked like the home of the Millionaire)
tock	the Syncopated Clock in the song of that name
todd-a-o	*Around the World in 80 Days* (with a cast of thousands)
tombstone territory	*The Tombstone* (Ariz.) *Epitaph*

tonight	In addition to Johnny Carson, name four men who have done the *TONIGHT* show on a regular basis.
tonto	*See* lone ranger.
topper	What were the names of the ghosts who came to haunt and help COSMO TOPPER? How did they die? What was the name of the often inebriated St. Bernard? Who played the role?
trent, helen	What was the theme song of *HELEN TRENT*? What question did the program ask?
true detective	What did the editor of *TRUE DETECTIVE* say at the end of his radio show?
truth or consequences	What was the name of the impatient buzzer on *TRUTH OR CONSEQUENCES?*
tubby	*See* lulu, little.

tonight	philosophical Steve Allen, jazzy Al "Jazzbo" Collins, smilin' Jack Lescoulie, and crying Jack Parr
topper	George and Marian Kirby
	in a car crash in the movie, but in an avalanche on television
	Neil; played by Buck
trent, helen	"Juanita"
	"Can a woman find happiness at 35—and even beyond?"
true detective	He described one of the nation's ten most wanted criminals and said, "If you have any information leading to the arrest of this man, contact either J. Edgar Hoover of the FBI or *me,* the editor of *True Detective.*"
truth or consequences	Beulah

twenty-one	Who defeated Charles Van Doren on *TWENTY-ONE?*
two for the money	Who emceed *"TWO FOR THE MONEY"?*
	What university president at one time verified the questions on this show?
umbrella	Who used an UMBRELLA as a sword?
uncle david	*See* goldberg, molly.
urecal, minerva	Name three television shows in which MINERVA URECAL regularly appeared.
values	When the VALUES go up, up, up And the prices go down, down, down—what's the reason?

twenty-one	Mrs. Vivienne Nearing
two for the money	Herb Shriner (later, Sam Levinson, who didn't use "Indiana" as a theme song)

Mason Gross (who at that time was professor of philosophy and provost at Rutgers) |
umbrella	Hiram Holliday, as played by the inimitable Wally Cox
urecal, minerva	*Tugboat Annie, Peter Gunn* (replacing Hope Emerson as Mother), and *Meet Mr. McNulty* (playing the role of a predictably stodgy president of a girls' college)
values	low overhead, low overhead (At least, that's the way Robert Hall explains it this season.)

vance, vivian	*See* frawley, william.
vaya con dios	Who sang "VAYA CON DIOS"?
velvet	Who starred in the movie, *NA-TIONAL VELVET?*
victory at sea	Who narrated *VICTORY AT SEA?*
video, captain	Who sponsored *CAPTAIN VIDEO?*
	Captain Video and the Ranger were played by _____ and _____.
	What was the name of their space ship?
volare	Who wrote and sang "VOLARE"?
voice of firestone	Who conducted the orchestra on *THE VOICE OF FIRESTONE?*
von climax	In what comic strip did APPASSIONATA VON CLIMAX appear?

vaya con dios	Les Paul and his one-time darling, Mary Ford
velvet	Elizabeth Taylor, who has since gone on to bigger and better things—like ranch mink, empress chinchilla . . .
victory at sea	Robert Graves
video, captain	Powerhouse candy bars Al Hodge and Bob Hastings The Galaxie
volare	Domenico Modugno
voice of firestone	Howard Barlow
von climax	*Li'l Abner*

wabbit	With whom do you associate the word "WABBIT"?
walsh, nobbie	Who played NOBBIE WALSH in the Joe Palooka movies?
waterfront	What was the name of Preston Foster's tugboat on *WATER-FRONT,* the television program?
watson, dr. john	*See* holmes, sherlock.
we're no angels	What was the name of the snake in *WE'RE NO ANGELS,* starring Humphrey Bogart, Aldo Ray and Peter Ustinov?
winter wonderland	In the meadow in WINTER WONDERLAND, what do you answer a mild-mannered snowman disguised as Parson Brown when he asks you, "Are you married?"
wizard, mr.	What did MR. WIZARD (Don Herbert) say about eating breakfast?

wabbit	Elmer Fudd *(q.v.)*
walsh, nobbie	James Gleason, Louis van Rooten, Leon Errol
waterfront	*The Cheryl Anne*
we're no angels	Adolph
winter wonderland	"No, man." (But suggest that the job is his when he's in town.)
wizard, mr.	"Scientists at a leading midwestern university have shown that students do better in school after they have eaten a nourishing breakfast. So be sure to start each day with a breakfast of fruit, cereal, milk, bread and butter, and possibly eggs or breakfast meats for variety."

wizard of oz	Who played the Tin Man, the Straw Man, the Lion and THE WIZARD OF OZ?
	What two characters did Margaret Hamilton play in the movie?
	Why is the wonderful Wizard of Oz a whiz?
	What were the lively little people in Oz country called?
wolf, li'l	What was the name of LI'L WOLF's father?
wolfman	Give the first line of this poem, spoken by the gypsy woman in the WOLFMAN movies— Maria Ouspenskaya: ". . . can become a wolf when the wolf-bane blooms and the autumn moon is bright."
woodchucks, junior	What is the *JUNIOR WOOD-CHUCK MANUAL?*
wuzzy, fuzzy	Complete the poem which begins: FUZZY WUZZY was a bear . . .

wizard of oz	Jack Haley, Ray Bolger, Burt Lahr, Frank Morgan
	the Wicked Witch of the West and Elvira Gulch
	"because of the wonderful things he does"
	Munchkins
wolf, li'l	Zeke (a wolf in cotton overalls who was always being wrongfully accused of stealing chickens)
wolfman	"Even he who is pure in heart and says his prayers by night . . ."
woodchucks, junior	the *Encyclopedia Britannica* and *What to Do Until the Doctor Comes* of Huey, Dewey and Louie—the amazing nephews of Donald Duck
wuzzy, fuzzy	. . . Fuzzy Wuzzy had no hair. Fuzzy Wuzzy wasn't fuzzy, was he?

xanadu

Who lived in opulent loneliness at the mansion called XANA-DU?

yankee doodle dandy

Who played George M. Cohan's father, mother, and sister in *YANKEE DOODLE DANDY?*

you are there

What was the theme music for *YOU ARE THERE?*

At the end of each program, what kind of day did Walter Cronkite say it had been?

you asked for it

What was the motto of the sponsor of *YOU ASKED FOR IT,* hosted by Art Baker?

you can't take it with you

What was the song Lionel Barrymore finally got Edward Arnold to sing in *YOU CAN'T TAKE IT WITH YOU?*

young, loretta

What was LORETTA YOUNG's announcer's first name?

117

xanadu	Citizen Charles Foster Kane
yankee doodle dandy	Walter Huston, Rosemary De Camp, and Jeanne Cagney
you are there	"Fanfare for the Common Man"
	A day like all days, filled with those events which alter and illuminate our times.
you asked for it	"If you like peanuts, you'll love Skippy."
you can't take it with you	"Polly Wolly Doodle"
young, loretta	John

118

young, mighty joe
Who reared **MIGHTY JOE YOUNG**?

young doctor malone
Who played **YOUNG DOCTOR MALONE** on radio and who played him on television?

young widder brown
Who was the announcer on *YOUNG WIDDER BROWN?*

zarkov, dr.
See gordon, flash.

zoo parade
Who was the host on *ZOO PARADE?*

zorro
What was **ZORRO's** father's name?

According to his theme song, when did Zorro ride?

119

young, mighty joe	Terry Moore
young doctor malone	Sandy Becker played the Three Oaks physician on radio, William Prince on television
young widder brown	George Ansborough
zoo parade	Marlin Perkins, then director of Chicago's Lincoln Park Zoo
zorro	Don Alexandro de la Vega was the father of Don Diego. When the full moon was bright

WHO SAID...?

1. "Bless your pea-pickin' little hearts."
2. "Coming, mother!"
3. "Dennis! Cut that out!"
4. "Don't fight it—it's bigger than both of us."
5. "Don't you cry—I'll be back again some day."
6. "Glad we could get together."
7. "Goodnight and good luck."
8. "Great Caesar's ghost!"
9. "Hey, Wild Bill! Wait for me!"
10. "Hi-ho, Steverino!"
11. "Huwaya, huwaya, huwaya."
12. "I'd like you to meet my brother George."
13. "I don't mess around, boy."
14. "I like it! I like it!"
15. "I never drink . . . wine."
16. "I think I can, I think I can, I think I can."
17. "I t'ought I taw a puddy tat . . . I did! I did taw a puddy tat."
18. "Ladies and gentlemen and all the ships at sea: let's go to press."
19. "One of these days . . . one of these days—POW! Right in the kisser!"
20. "Put a little fun in your life—try dancing."
21. "So long and be good to yourself."
22. "Strange things are happening."

1. Tennessee Ernie Ford
2. Henry Aldrich
3. Jack Benny, to Dennis Day (Although Henry Mitchel and his neighbor, Mr. Wilson, probably also said it to Dennis the Menace on occasion.)
4. Maxine, secretary to Uncle Miltie
5. Frosty the Snowman
6. John Cameron Swayze
7. Edward R. Murrow, on *Person to Person*
8. Perry White, "chief" to Clark Kent, Jimmy Olsen, Lois Lane, *et al.*
9. Jingles (Andy Devine)
10. Gordon Hathaway (Louis Nye)
11. Arthur "Flow-Thru Tea Bag" Godfrey
12. Liberace
13. Ricky Nelson
14. Jerry Lewis
15. Count Voivode Dracula, who had other ways of quenching his thirst
16. The Little Engine That Could
17. Tweety, who taw Sylvester
18. Walter Winchell
19. Ralph Kramden (Jackie Gleason), to his wife, Alice (Audrey Meadows)
20. Kathryn Murray, Arthur's wife
21. Don MacNeil, on *The Breakfast Club,* from Chicago
22. Red Buttons, who died on television and then made a comeback by committing suicide in the movie, *Sayonara*

23. "Sufferin' succotash!"
24. "To be sure, Queenie!"
25. "Well, I'll be a dirty bird!"
26. "What a revoltin' development *this* is!"
27. "Why don't you pick me up and smoke me sometime?"
28. "Would *you* like to be Queen for a Day?"
29. "You call me, Papa?"
30. "You rang?"

23. Daffy Duck, perhaps the wackiest duck in all of comic literature
24. Boston Blackie
25. Lonesome George Gobel
26. Chester A. Riley
27. Edie Adams, when she was impersonating a Muriel cigar
28. Jack Bailey
29. Rosa, Pasquali's fat daughter on *Life with Luigi*
30. Maynard G. Krebs (Bob Denver)

TWENTY TRIVIA QUESTIONS FOR THE CONNOISSEUR

Obviously, there are a great many superb Trivia questions to challenge the confident Trivia player. Here are twenty such emotion-packed problems at a high degree of obscurity. If you score above 16, you're quite good; if you score below 6, you're rather poor.

1. Name Milton Berle's mother.
2. Who starred in Alfred Hitchcock's original production of *Thirty-Nine Steps?*
3. What is the name of Edgar Bergen's only female puppet?
4. What was Superman's name on the planet Krypton?
5. What was the name of the character portrayed by Broderick Crawford in *All the King's Men?*
6. Who portrayed The Old Ranger on *Death Valley Days?*
7. What group sang the hit version of "Goodnight, Irene"?
8. Who was the bald, sourpuss comedian who appeared in most Laurel and Hardy movies?
9. What wrestler was known as "the little flower"?
10. Who, in comic literature, owns the biggest ball of string in the world?
11. What television series featured Mitzi Green, Gordon Jones, Jimmy Lydon and Virginia Gibson?
12. In *High Sierra,* what was the name of the dog Ida Lupino and Humphrey Bogart became attached to?
13. What was the name of Captain Midnight's airplane?
14. Give the radio and television casts of *Gunsmoke.*
15. What were the first names of Mama and her sisters?

1. Sandra
2. Robert Donat and Madeleine Carroll
3. Effie Clinker
4. Kal-El
5. Willie Stark
6. Stanley Andrews
7. The Weavers
8. Jimmy Finlayson
9. Benito Gardenia
10. $crooge OK McDuck
11. *So This Is Hollywood*
12. Pard
13. *The Silver Dart*
14. Marshal Matt Dillon: William Conrad (radio) and James Arness (television)
    Chester: Parley Baer (radio) and Dennis Weaver (television)
    Doc: Howard McNeer (radio) and Milburn Stone (television)
    Kitty: Georgia Ellis (radio) and Amanda Blake (television)
15. Martha ("Marta"), Jenny ("Yenny") and Trina ("Trina")

16. At what school did Our Miss Brooks teach?
17. What kind of people-eater did Sheb Wooley sing about?
18. Who moderated *Quiz Kids?*
19. What was the title of Bishop Fulton J. Sheen's television show?
20. Who is Humphrey Pennyworth?

16. Madison High School
17. one-eyed, one-horned, flying, purple
18. Clifton Fadiman on TV—Joe Kelly on radio
19. *Life Is Worth Living*
20. Joe Palooka's plump pal

Trivia

PHOTO-QUIZ
(Answers on last page)

1. In what picture was this scene and who
sang the romantic leads?

129

2. With what two songs is this woman
best associated?

3. How was this hot-hoofed wonder beast described on the program where it played opposite Scout?

4. Name these characters, the actors who portrayed them, and their dog.

5. Who are these noteworthy gentlemen
   and what are they talking about?

6. Who is missing from this scene?

7. These, of course, are all members in good standing of Our Gang. Can you name them?

8. What's the name of the movie this scene is taken from and on what island did the story take place?

9. This hero was called "O. Henry's Robin Hood of The Old West." The same actor portrayed him in movies and on television—who is he?

10. Who created this thirsty resident of Transylvania?

11. What was the name of King Kong's
captor and who played him?

MORE TRIVIAL
Trivia

PHOTO-QUIZ
(Answers on last page)

12 —GROUCHO MARX was to GEORGE FENNEMAN
   what this man was to _____

13 —What was this man's favorite sport?

14—Who is this heroine and what did she confront during each exciting episode of a well known serial?

15 —Why is this cowboy different from all other cowboys?

139

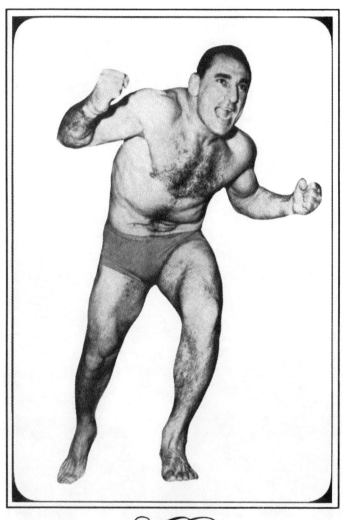

16—This man's native country is a. Vietnam
b. Argentina c. Disneyland d. Transylvania
e. None of these four

17—Who are these lovers-to-be? In what well-known
movie does this scene appear?

18—Who is this man?

19—And this?

20—Who was the Scotland Yard official who frequently asked for the aid of these two sleuths? a. $crooge McDuck b. Charlie Chan c. Commisioner Gordon d. Timothy Geoghegan e. Inspector La Strade

21—This precocious young couple (no longer a couple) is: a. Eddie and Debbie b. Eddie and Liz c. Richard and Liz d. Richard and Debbie e. Eddie and Richard

22—This man is: a. The Thin Man b. Dr. Frankenstein
c. Igor d. The Mummy e. The Creature from the
Black Lagoon

23 —In one of their films, these two belonged to a
fraternal organization with the same name as
the movie. The name is: a. Junior Woodchucks
b. Loyal Order of Raccoons c. Sons of the Desert
d. Mystic Knights of the Sea e. Hadassah

MORE TRIVIAL
TRIVIAL

Trivia

abner, li'l

Who married LI'L ABNER and Daisy Mae?

Who is the ugliest woman in Lower Slobbovia (and the rest of the world, too)?

affair to remember, an

The Cary Grant-Deborah Kerr film, *AN AFFAIR TO REMEMBER,* was a remake of a Charles Boyer movie. What was its name and who was Boyer's co-star?

ameche, don

What constantly spatting couple did DON AMECHE and Frances Langford portray?

amos 'n' andy

Who was the janitor at the Mystic Knights of the Sea Lodge Hall?

What were the names of AMOS's wife and daughter?

andrews, archie

What school did ARCHIE ANDREWS and his friends attend?

abner, li'l	Marryin' Sam, the last man you'd want to meet on Sadie Hawkins Day
	Lena the Hyena (Obviously someone put the double whammy on her.)
affair to remember, an	*Love Affair;* Irene Dunne
ameche, don	The Bickersons (who got their start on radio with Bob Hope)
amos 'n' andy	Lightnin' (played by Nick O'Demus)
	Ruby and Arbadella
andrews, archie	Riverdale High School, scene of many confrontations between Jughead and Miss Grundy

applewhite, charlie

What television super-star brought singer CHARLIE APPLEWHITE to fame?

armstrong, jack

What high school did JACK ARMSTRONG go to?

Who was the announcer on Jack's program?

arrow, broken

Who were the stars of *BROKEN ARROW* and what characters did they portray?

atlas, charles

What did CHARLES ATLAS call his method for making he-men of 97-pound weaklings?

How long were the daily exercises he prescribed?

Who was Atlas's main competitor in the muscle-building industry?

applewhite, charlie	Milton Berle
armstrong, jack	Hudson Franklin MacCormack
arrow, broken	Michael Ansara played Chief Cochise and John Lupton played Tom Jeffers, the Indian agent.
atlas, charles	"Dynamic Tension," which certainly seemed worth gambling a stamp on 15 minutes a day George F. Jowett

badfellows, dis-
loyal order of

Who was the most famous mem-
ber of the DISLOYAL OR-
DER OF BADFELLOWS?

ballet

What wrestler brought the art of
BALLET into the ring with
him?

ballin' the jack

When you're BALLIN' THE
JACK, how do you do the
eagle walk?

b'ar

See crockett, davy.

babar

BABAR the Elephant's wife
was————————.

bazooka

How did BAZOOKA, the
Atom Bubble Boy, fly?

What did he say to descend?

bathing suit

She wore a very scanty, light-
colored, spotted BATHING
SUIT. Describe it more pre-
cisely.

bedbugs

If you see any BEDBUGS on
me, what should you do?

badfellows, disloyal order of	Zeke Wolf, father of Li'l Bad
ballet	Ricky Starr, whose talent for arabesques never hindered his dropkicks one bit
ballin' the jack	With style and grace (and with your lovin' arms spread right out in space)
babar	La belle Celeste
bazooka	He said, "Bazooka, Bazooka, make me a bubble—and fly me to where my good friends are in trouble!" Then he blew a huge bubble and flew to where his good friends were in trouble.

"Akoozab! Akoozab!" (Clever, huh?) |
| bathing suit | Itsy-bitsy, teeny-weeny, yellow polka-dot bikini |
| bedbugs | Take a few. |

believe it or not	What is the name of the column that ran in competition with Robert Ripley's "BELIEVE IT OR NOT," and who wrote it?
bellamy, ralph	Name the detective played by RALPH BELLAMY in the television series, *Man Against Crime.*
belvedere, mr.	What actor portrayed MR. BELVEDERE, jack of all trades and master of every one of them?
benny, jack	What make car did JACK BENNY drive and who supplied the mechanical coughing and wheezing?
	Who was Jack's Spanish-speaking acquaintance?
	Who was this man's Spanish-speaking sister?
	What did she do for a living?
bergman, ingrid	Whom did INGRID BERGMAN portray in *The Bells of St. Mary's?*

believe it or not	"Strange as It Seems" by John Hix, believe it or not
bellamy, ralph	Mike Barnett
belvedere, mr.	Clifton Webb
benny, jack	Maxwell; Mel Blanc, the man with the magic vocal cords Sy (Si, Sy.) Sue Sew
bergman, ingrid	Sister Benedict (Bing Crosby played Father "Dial 'O' For" O'Malley, the reformed pianist who saw to it that the movie had a happy ending.)

berkeley, busby	Who sang the immortal BUSBY BERKELEY number, "Remember My Forgotten Man," in *Gold Diggers of 1933?*
	Who sang "We're in the Money" in pig Latin in the same film?
big town	For what outfit did Steve Wilson work in *BIG TOWN?*
	Who was Steve's secretary?
bill and coo	Who were the Academy Award-winning BILL AND COO?
bill, congo	Who was CONGO BILL's faithful companion?
blues, pete kelly's	Who starred in the movie, *PETE KELLY'S BLUES?*
	Who had the lead role in the short-lived television series?
bob and ray	Who was the news reporter created by BOB AND RAY?

berkeley, busby	Joan Blondell
	Ginger Rogers (The picture also starred Ruby Keeler and Aline MacMahon.)
big town	*The Illustrated Press*
	Lorelei Kilbourne (Steve was originally played by Edward G. Robinson, Lorelei by Claire Trevor.)
bill and coo	A pair of awfully sharp birds, who probably enjoyed perching on their Oscar
bill, congo	Janu the Jungle Boy
blues, pete	Jack Webb
kelly's	Bill Reynolds
bob and ray	Wally Ballou, the man with the nasal voice

bogart,
humphrey

What did HUMPHREY BO-GART permit Lauren Bacall to do in his office in *The Big Sleep?*

Who starred with Bogie in *Treasure of the Sierra Madre?*

What accident befell H. B. in *They Drive by Night?*

At the end of *Casablanca,* what did Louie, the prefect of police, discard in a trash can?

What was the name of Sam Spade's detective agency?

bolger, ray

What song is best associated with RAY BOLGER? From what show?

boy

See tarzan.

boys, beagle

What three digits were common to all the BEAGLE BOYS' prison numbers?

bogart, humphrey	Scratch her leg
	Walter Huston and Tim Holt
	He lost an arm when his truck careened off the road.
	A bottle of Vichy water
	Archer and Spade
bolger, ray	"Once in Love with Amy," from *Where's Charlie?*
boys, beagle	1, 6, 7 (The order of these and additional digits varied.)

boys, bowery	Who was "the nice kid" in the BOWERY BOYS series (Sam Katzman's offshoot of the Dead End Kids)?
	In the same series, who played Scroono?
bravados, the	In the movie, *THE BRAVADOS,* who did it?
brando, marlon	In what movie did MARLON BRANDO play the leader of a motorcycle gang that terrorized a small town?
break the bank	Who hosted *BREAK THE BANK?*
brown, johnny mack	Who joined up with JOHNNY MACK BROWN to form the trio known as The Range Riders?
brother rat	Who played the illegally married cadet in *BROTHER RAT?*

boys, bowery	Danny (played by Bobby Jordan) "Sunshine Sammy" Morrison, one of the original "Our Gang" kids
bravados, the	Butler, the ranch owner next door
brando, marlon	*The Wild One*
break the bank	Bud Collyer on radio, Bert Parks on television
brown, johnny mack	Raymond Hatton and Tim Mc-Coy
brother rat	Eddie Albert

burgess, thornton w.	Who inhabited the Green Forest, the Laughing Brook, the Smiling Pond, the Crooked Little Path and the other places created by the prolific writer, THORNTON W. BURGESS?
caesar, little	What was the name of the criminal played by Edward G. Robinson in *LITTLE CAESAR?*
caesar, sid	What was the name of the family portrayed by SID CAESAR and Imogene Coca on *Your Show of Shows?*
	What was the name of Caesar's bespectacled jazz saxophonist (not to be confused with Progress Hornsby, another jazz man, who did not wear glasses)?
cagney, james	In what picture did JAMES CAGNEY grind a grapefruit into a girl's face?
	Who was the unlucky girl?

burgess, thornton w.	Buster Bear, Jimmy Skunk, Bobby Coon, Farmer Brown, Bowser the Hound, Sammy Jay, Old Mr. Toad, Yowler the Bobcat, Paddy the Beaver, Prickly Porky the Porcupine, Little Joe Otter, Lightfoot the Deer, Mr. Blacksnake, Reddy Fox, Unc' Billy Possum, Hooty the Great Horned Owl, Blacky the Crow, Johnny Chuck, Happy Jack the Gray Squirrel, Jennie Wren, Robber the Rat, Old Mother Nature and her assorted winds, coyotes and many other friends
caesar, little	Caesar Enrique Bandello
caesar, sid	The Hickenloopers Cool Cees
cagney, james	*Public Enemy* Mae Clark

caine's hundred

Who starred in the not too successful *CAINE'S HUNDRED*, a series that dealt with one man's campaign against the 100 top criminals in society?

cantor, eddie

What was EDDIE CANTOR's closing song on each radio show?

carolina rice

What can be finer than a box of CAROLINA RICE, so nice?

caspar

What kind of ghost was CASPAR?

cat, felix the

What was FELIX THE CAT's favorite mode of transportation?

cheyenne

What was CHEYENNE's last name?

Who played that tall wanderer?

chips, mr.

Who starred as the dedicated school teacher in *GOOD-BY MR. CHIPS?*

caine's hundred	Mark Richmond
cantor, eddie	"I love to spend every Thursday with you;
	And as friend to friend, I'm sorry it's through."
carolina rice	Nothing
caspar	Friendly
cat, felix	His magic flying carpet
cheyenne	Bodie
	Clint Walker
chips, mr.	Robert Donat

cinemiracle

What was the first film made by the technique called "CINE-MIRACLE"?

coates, paul

What controversial interview program was hosted by PAUL COATES?

cole, old king

What did OLD KING COLE call for?

colgate

What does COLGATE toothpaste do while it cleans your teeth?

colt .45

Who starred as the inventor of the historic COLT .45 on the television show of the same name?

como, perry

What song introduced the request part of PERRY COMO's program?

composers

What actors are associated with the following COMPOSERS: Robert Schuman, Franz Liszt, and Johannes Brahms?

cinemiracle	*Windjammer*
coates, paul	*Confidential File*
cole, old king	His pipe, his bowl and three violinists
colgate	It guards your breath. (What a toothpaste!)
colt .45	Wade Preston (as Sam Colt)
como, perry	"Letters, we get letters, we get stacks and stacks of letters. . . . Dear Perry, would you be so kind as to grant a request and sing the song I like best?"
composers	Paul Henreid, Dirk Bogarde and Robert Walker

cooper, gary	What movie starred GARY COOPER in the role of Wild Bill Hickok?
copperfield, david	Who played the title role in the movie, *DAVID COPPERFIELD?*
	Who played Mr. Micawber?
cotten, joseph	What kind of writer did JOSEPH COTTEN play in *The Third Man?*
court of last resort	Who played the chief investigator of the COURT OF LAST RESORT, an organization that saved the innocent once a week?
crockett, davy	How old was DAVY CROCKETT when he killed him a b'ar?
crosby, bob	What group sang regularly with BOB CROSBY's band on his television show?
	What was the band's name?

cooper, gary	*The Plainsman* (Jean Arthur played his lady love, Calamity Jane.)
copperfield, david	Freddie Bartholomew W. C. Fields
cotten, joseph	A writer of Westerns
court of last resort	Lyle Bettger
crockett, davy	Only three
crosby, bob	The Modernaires The Bobcats

crusader
Who starred in *CRUSADER?*

What character did he play?

cummings, bob
Who played Schultzie on *The BOB CUMMINGS Show?*

Who played Pamela Livingstone (accent on the "stone")?

What was Bob's field of work on the show?

What was his first television show—before *The Bob Cummings Show?*

daisy
What colorful Western hero endorsed DAISY air rifles?

dallas, stella
What was the story of STELLA DALLAS all about?

What was the name of Stella's son-in-law?

dangerous assignment
What famous tough villain in the movies turned over a new leaf and became a tough hero on the television series, *DANGEROUS ASSIGNMENT?*

169

crusader	Brian Keith played Matt Anders (né Andrewski).
cummings, bob	Ann B. Davis
	Nancy Culp
	Fashion photography
	My Hero

daisy	Red Ryder
dallas, stella	Mother love and sacrifice (according to its creator, Olive Higgins Prouty)
	Richard Grovesnor
dangerous assignment	Brian Donleavy

death valley days	Who sponsored *DEATH VALLEY DAYS?*
de bergerac, cyrano	Who played Roxanne opposite Jose Ferrer's CYRANO DE BERGERAC?
dick and jane	DICK AND JANE had a dog. Dick and Jane had a cat. Name Dick's and Jane's dog and cat.
disneyland	Name the four subdivisions of DISNEYLAND.
district attorney, mr.	What did MR. DISTRICT ATTORNEY solemnly swear to do about the rights and privileges of the citizens of his community?
	Who sponsored Mr. D. A.?
dollar, johnny	What was JOHNNY DOLLAR's occupation?

death valley days	Boraxo (The commercials were done by Rosemary De Camp, her four daughters and 20 mules.)
de bergerac, cyrano	Mala Powers
dick and jane	Their dog was named Spot. Their cat was named Puff.
disneyland	Adventureland, Tomorrowland, Frontierland, and Fantasyland, the happiest land of them all
district attorney, mr.	To defend them with equal vigor Sal Hepatica
dollar, johnny	Insurance investigator (His hobby was adding up his expense account.)

doody, howdy	What was the name of HOWDY DOODY's lovely princess friend?
	What was John J. Fadoozle's title?
	Name Flubberdub's favorite food.
dracula, count	What is the only way to kill COUNT DRACULA?
	Who discovered this neck-relieving method?
drew, nancy	NANCY DREW was a girl――――.
dreyfus, capt.	CAPT. DREYFUS was portrayed in *The Life of Emile Zola* and in *I Accuse*. Who played him in each?
duck soup	Who played the prosecuting attorney in the Marx Brothers' film, *DUCK SOUP*?
	What was the national anthem of the country depicted in the movie?

doody, howdy	Princess Summerfallwinterspring
	"America's No. One (Boing!) Private Eye"
	Spaghetti (pronounced "pizghetti")
dracula, count	Drive a wooden stake through his heart (You could also keep him on a very restricted bloodless diet.)
	Dr. Von Helsing
drew, nancy	Detective (the second oldest profession)
dreyfus, capt.	Joseph Schildkraut; José Ferrer
duck soup	Charles Middleton (who also played Ming the Merciless in the Flash Gordon serials)
	"Hail Fredonia"

duggan, andrew

What two Warner Brothers' television presentations starred ANDREW DUGGAN?

earp, wyatt

According to the song, what three adjectives best describe WYATT EARP?

What three men played Wyatt on the television series, in the movie, *My Darling Clementine,* and in the movie, *Gunfight at O.K. Corral?*

edge of night, the

What was the profession of the hero of *THE EDGE OF NIGHT?*

Who played him?

ehrlich, dr. paul

Who portrayed microbe-hunter *DR. PAUL EHRLICH* in the film about him?

Name that film.

duggan, andrew	*Bourbon Street Beat; Room for One More*
earp, wyatt	Brave, courageous and bold
	Hugh O'Brian, Henry Fonda, Burt Lancaster
edge of night, the	Assistant district attorney
	John Larkin
ehrlich, dr. paul	Edward G. Robinson
	Dr. Ehrlich's Magic Bullet

end, dead — Which former *DEAD END* kid regularly imitated Bela Lugosi on *The Steve Allen Show?*

everly brothers — Where was little Suzie sleeping when the EVERLY BROTH-ERS tried to wake her up?

falcon, the — What actor is most closely associated with the character of THE FALCON in the movies?

falls, hawkins — Who did the commercials on the television soap opera, *HAW-KINS FALLS?*

farmer's daughter — Who played the FARMER'S DAUGHTER in the movie?

fink, big mike — What was BIG MIKE FINK's title in the Davy Crockett episodes on television?

What do men and girls do at the mere thought of Big Mike?

end, dead   Gabriel Dell

everly brothers   In a movie theater (The movie was over and they were in trouble deep.)

falcon, the   Tom Conway (On television, Charles McGraw played that feared enemy of the underworld.)

falls, hawkins   Hugh Downs

farmer's daughter   Loretta Young, who later made it big on television gliding through doorways (She never did trip on her gown.)

fink, big mike   "King of the River"
Men all shout, girls all shiver.

firestone, voice of	Who was the announcer on *VOICE OF FIRESTONE?*
flash, the	How did THE FLASH acquire his great speed?
forty-second street	In *FORTY-SECOND STREET,* a musical about the wonderful world of show biz, who sprained her ankle and gave Ruby Keeler her big chance?
	In the same film, who was "sugar daddy" to Ginger Rogers?
frankenstein	Complete the following: "Henry is a friend of mine; he resembles FRANKENSTEIN . . ."
frankenstein, bride of	In *BRIDE OF FRANKENSTEIN,* Elsa Lanchester played a double role. One was the lovely bride. What was the other?
fu, egg	Whose enemy was EGG FU?

firestone, voice of	Ed James
flash, the	He inhaled the fumes from an explosion in his chemistry lab.
forty-second street	Bebe Daniels Guy Kibbee
Frankenstein	". . . for a nickel or a dime, fifty cents for overtime."
frankenstein, bride of	Mary Shelley author of *Frankenstein*
fu, egg	Wonder Woman's

gallant, capt.	What father-and-son team starred in *CAPTAIN GALLANT OF THE FOREIGN LEGION?*
	What last outpost of the Foreign Legion did these two help patrol?
glomgold, flintheart	Who is FLINTHEART GLOMGOLD?
giant	Name the four stars of *GIANT*.
gildersleeve, the great	What was THE GREAT GILDERSLEEVE's first name?
	What was his appointed title?
	What was the name of his druggist friend?
	His nephew? His maid?
godfrey, arthur	Who led the band on television for ARTHUR GODFREY and his friends?
	Who was Arthur's Irish songstress?

gallant, capt.	The Crabbes—Larry ("Buster") and Cullen ("Cuffy")
	Northern Africa
glomgold, flintheart	The South African mine owner who once claimed to be the richest duck in the world, but grudgingly deferred to Uncle $crooge when the old miser showed that his ball of string was the larger
giant	James Dean, Rock Hudson, Liz Taylor, Jo Van Fleet
gildersleeve, the great	Throckmorton
	Water Commissioner
	"Peavie"
	Leroy; Birdie
godfrey, arthur	Archie Bleyer
	Carmel Quinn

going my way	What were the names of the two priests in GOING MY WAY?
gone with the wind	Name the actors who played Scarlet O'Hara's husbands in GONE WITH THE WIND.
goofy	What was the name of GOOFY's brilliant nephew?
	What did he wear on his head?
great dictator, the	Who played the Mussolini character in Charlie Chaplin's THE GREAT DICTATOR?
grand hotel	Who starred in GRAND HOTEL?
green hornet	What did the GREEN HORNET use for a garage for his car, Black Beauty?
	What was the Hornet's identity?
	Who said at the end of many *Green Hornet* adventures, "Sufferin' snakes, Reid, the Hornet's done it again!"

going my way	Father O'Malley, played by Bing Crosby (*See* bergman, ingrid), and Father FitzGibbon, played by Barry Fitzgerald
gone with the wind	Rand Brooks, Carroll Nye, Clark Gable
goofy	Gilbert (who, despite his genius, could never quite figure out his Uncle Goofy)
	A mortarboard
great dictator, the	Jack Oakie, who in the movies was more often seen in the company of Jack Haley
grand hotel	Greta Garbo, Wallace Beery, John and Lionel Barrymore, Joan Crawford, and Lewis Stone
green hornet	"A seemingly abandoned warehouse"
	Britt Reid, publisher of *The Daily Sentinel*
	Michael Axford, the troubleshooting reporter on the *Sentinel*

green lantern	What was the GREEN LAN-TERN's real name?
	Where did he get his power?
	What was his oath?
gumby	What was GUMBY's pet pony called?
gumps, the	Who was named Bim in "THE GUMPS?"
	What was Andy's wife's name?
gunga din	Who starred in *GUNGA DIN?*
gunn, peter	What was the name of the police lieutenant on *PETER GUNN?*

green lantern	Alan Scott (an engineer)
	From his power ring, which he charged with the lantern given to him by the Guardians of the Universe
	In brightest day, In blackest night, No evil shall escape my sight. Let those who worship evil's night Beware my power—Green Lantern's light.
gumby	Pokey
gumps, the	Andy's millionaire uncle Min
gunga din	Cary Grant, Douglas Fairbanks, Jr., Victor McLaglen (Sam Jaffe, later Ben Casey's superior, Dr. Zorba, was Gunga Din.)
gunn, peter	Jacoby, played by Herschel Bernardi

186

hadley, reed   In what two television series did REED HADLEY play a man on the right side of the law?

hardy, andy   In what town did ANDY HARDY and his family live?

What actress played the New York girl who fell in love with Andy?

harris, phil   PHIL HARRIS's wife's name:

_____.

harum, david   What type of horse did Will Rogers race in *DAVID HARUM?*

havoc, june   What was the name of JUNE HAVOC's television series?

What part did she play?

hawk, henery   Who was HENERY HAWK's best friend, in "Looney Tunes and Merrie Melodies" comics?

heckle and jeckle   What kind of birds were HECKLE AND JECKLE, the airborne Chip and Dale?

hadley, reed	*Racket Squad* and *Public Defender*
hardy, andy	Carvel Judy Garland, as Betsy Booth
harris, phil	Alice Faye
harum, david	A trotter
havoc, june	*Willy* Willy Dodger
hawk, henery	Ollie Owl
heckle and jeckle	Magpies

heidi

With whom did HEIDI live?

Who played Shirley Temple's grandfather in the film version of *Heidi?*

henry viii

In the movie, *THE PRIVATE LIFE OF HENRY VIII,* who played Henry and who played Anne of Cleves?

hideaway, hernando's

How do you gain admittance to HERNANDO'S HIDE-AWAY?

hilltop house

HILLTOP HOUSE was a soap opera about _____.

Who was playing the lead role at the time that *Hilltop House* disappeared from the radio waves forever?

his honor homer bell

HIS HONOR HOMER BELL starred _____.

What was His Honor's niece's name?

heidi	Her grandfather and his goat
	Jean Hersholt (radio's Dr. Christian)
henry viii	Charles Laughton and Elsa Lanchester
hideaway, hernando's	Knock three times and whisper low that you and I were sent by Joe.
hilltop house	Life at an orphanage
	Jan Miner
his honor homer bell	Gene Lockhart
	Casey

hope, bob	Name BOB HOPE's two radio bandleaders.
	Who was his announcer on radio?
hotel de paris	Who starred in the television Western series, *HOTEL DE PARIS?*
	What was the name of the character he played and what was so unusual about his Western garb?
hutton, ina ray	What was INA RAY HUTTON's claim to musical fame?
hutton, robert	Whom did ROBERT HUTTON want to have a date with in *Hollywood Canteen?*
	Did he get the date?
if i were king	What figure did Ronald Coleman portray in the film *IF I WERE KING?*

hope, bob	Skinnay Ennis and Les Brown Bill Goodwin
hotel de paris	Earl Holliman His name was Sundance and he wore a golden chain around his black hat, to catch the sun's rays and reflect them into the eyes of his opponents in gun duels.
hutton, ina ray	She was the leader of an all-girl band.
hutton, robert	Joan Leslie Yes.
if i were king	François Villon, the French vaga-bond-poet

incredible shrinking man, the	What did THE INCREDIBLE SHRINKING MAN try to eat when he was teeny-weeny (before he became itsy-bitsy)?
information please	Who were the regular panelists on *INFORMATION PLEASE?*
informer, the	Who played the leading role in *THE INFORMER?*
inner sanctum	Who was the host of *INNER SANCTUM?*
in old chicago	Who starred in *IN OLD CHICAGO,* a picture ostensibly about the Chicago fire and the cow that caused it?
i.q., doctor	Who was a regular on *DOCTOR I.Q.* (besides the doc)?
i remember mama	Who played Mama and Papa in the *movie* version of *I REMEMBER MAMA?*
i spy	Who was the host of the original *I SPY* show on television?

incredible shrinking man, the	Cheese he found in a mousetrap, but was unsuccessful in freeing
information please	John Kieran and Franklin P. Adams (Oscar Levant, Clifton Fadiman and Groucho Marx were among the frequent visitors.)
informer, the	Victor McLaglen, as Gypo, a mercenary fink
inner sanctum	Paul McGrath
in old chicago	Alice Faye and Don Ameche
i.q., doctor	The Lady in the Balcony
i remember mama	Irene Dunne and Philip Dorn (not to be confused with television's Peggy Wood and Judson Laire)
i spy	Raymond Massey

it happened
one night

What song was sung during a
bus ride in the film *IT HAP-
PENED ONE NIGHT?*

ivy, halls of

Who starred in *HALLS OF
IVY,* the television series about
the life of the president of a
small college?

jane

See dick and jane.

jones, lorenzo

What was the name of inventor
LORENZO JONES's wife?

What was the show's theme song?

jones, spike

Who was the midget on *The
SPIKE JONES Show?*

Who was the show's regular female vocalist?

j'onzz, j'onn

When J'ONN J'ONZZ visited
Earth from his native Mars,
what name did he assume?

What was he called?

it happened one night	"The Daring Young Man on the Flying Trapeze" (sung by nearly everybody in the bus)
ivy, halls of	Ronald Coleman and his wife Benita, who played the Todhunter-Halls

jones, lorenzo	Belle "Funiculi, Funicula"
jones, spike	Billy Barty Helen Greco (Spike's wife)
j'onzz, j'onn	John Jones (Clever, huh?) "Manhunter from Mars"

kabibble, ish	With whose band did ISH KA-BIBBLE play?
katrinka	*See* toonerville trolley.
katzenjammer kids	Under what other name has "THE KATZENJAMMER KIDS" appeared?
kazootie, rootie	What is ROOTIE KAZOOTIE full of?
kemosabe	*See* lone ranger, the.
key largo	Who played Edward G. Robinson's alcoholic moll in *KEY LARGO?*
kildare, doctor	In the movie series, *DOCTOR KILDARE,* what was the name of the head of Blair General Hospital?
	Which head nurse managed to get the better of Dr. Gillespie more often than not?
	Which nurse did Dr. Gillespie take delight in tormenting?
king, rocky	Who was the sponsor of *ROCKY KING, Detective?*
	Who played Rocky?

kabibble, ish	Kay Kyser's
katzenjammer kids	"The Captain and the Kids" (same captain, same kids)
kazootie, rootie	Zip and joy
key largo	Claire Trevor
kildare, dr.	Dr. Walter Carew Molly Byrd Nurse Parker
king, rocky	Sano cigarettes William Gargan

knickerbocker
holiday

Who played Peter Stuyvesant in
the movie version of *KNICK-
ERBOCKER HOLIDAY?*

What famous song did he sing?

kryptonite

What is the usual color of the
primary isotope of KRYPTO-
NITE?

lady takes a
chance, the

Who starred in *THE LADY
TAKES A CHANCE,* the
story of an Eastern girl who
set her heart on nabbing a
tall, roaming cowhand?

lane, bronco

How did BRONCO LANE get
his name?

Who played him on television?

life begins at 80

Who sponsored *LIFE BEGINS
AT 80?*

Who hosted the show?

knickerbocker holiday	Charles Coburn "September Song"
kryptonite	Green
lady takes a chance, the	Jean Arthur and John Wayne (The busdriver was Phil Silvers—*See* you'll never get rich.)
lane, bronco	"There ain't a horse that he can't handle—that's how he got his name." Ty Hardin
life begins at 80	Geritol (Who else?) Jack Barry (of *Juvenile Jury* and *Winky Dink and You* fame, and also of *Twenty-one*)

life with father	What family was portrayed in *LIFE WITH FATHER?*
	Who played mother and father on television?
little, stuart	What was STUART LITTLE?
live television	What do the numbers "90" and "one" have to do with LIVE TELEVISION drama?
lone ranger, the	What does *kemosabe* mean?
	Where were the Texas Rangers ambushed?
	Who betrayed them by leading them into the ambush of the Cavendish gang?
	Who saved THE LONE RANGER?
lone wolf, the	What swashbuckling movie star appeared as a private investigator in the television series, *THE LONE WOLF?*
lost horizon	In *LOST HORIZON,* Ronald Coleman fell in love with a woman more than 100 years old. Who played her?
	Where did she live?
	What part did Sam Jaffe play in that film?

life with father	The Clarence Days
	Lureen Tuttle ("Vinny") and Leon Ames ("Clare")
little, stuart	A nattily attired mouse
live television	They should make you think of *Playhouse 90* and *Studio One*.
lone ranger, the	Faithful friend
	In Bryant's Gap
	Their guide, Collins
	Tonto, who dug six graves for the five dead rangers to fool Cavendish into thinking all the rangers had died
lone wolf, the	Louis Hayward
lost horizon	Jane Wyatt
	Shangri-La
	The centuries-old Grand Lama

lost weekend	Who starred in *LOST WEEK-END?*
love and marriage	LOVE AND MARRIAGE go together like _____.
lulu, little	What was LITTLE LULU's last name?
	What kind of berry populated the forest around Witch Hazel's home?
lundigan, william	What was the name of the television drama series WILLIAM LUNDIGAN hosted?
mae, daisy	What was DAISY MAE's maiden name?
maisie	Who played the title role in the MAISIE series in the movies?
mañana	For whom is MANANA soon enough?

lost weekend	Ray Milland (as the alcoholic) and Jane Wyman
love and marriage	A horse and carriage
lulu, little	Moppet
	Beebleberries, a cross between bananas and Spam
lundigan, william	*Climax*
mae, daisy	Daisy Mae Scragg, a name which doesn't really describe her too well
maisie	Ann Sothern (who made it big on television playing Suzie McNamara)
mañana	Me

malone, young dr.	What was YOUNG DR. MALONE's first name?
man behind the badge, the	Who was the host-narrator of *THE MAN BEHIND THE BADGE?*
man who came to dinner, the	In *THE MAN WHO CAME TO DINNER,* what was the name of the nurse who got on Sheridan Whiteside's nerves?
marty	In the film, *MARTY,* what did MARTY (Ernest Borgnine) do for a living?
	Who played the girl he finally met?
	Where did he meet her?
marvel, captain	What was CAPTAIN MARVEL's secret identity?
	What was his occupation and for whom did he work?
	What did Dr. Sivana call him?
marvel, captain, jr.	What was CAPTAIN MARVEL, JR.'s secret identity?
	What did he say to become marvelously powerful? (He did *not* say "SHAZAM!")

malone, young dr.	Jerry
man behind the badge, the	Charles Bickford
man who came to dinner, the	Miss Preen, played by Virginia Wickes (Monty Woolley was Sherry.)
marty	He was a butcher.
	Betsy Blair
	At a dance hall
marvel, captain	Billy Batson
	He was a boy reporter for WHIZ radio.
	"That big red cheese"
marvel, captain, jr.	Freddie Freeman, the crippled newsboy
	"CAPTAIN MARVEL!"

marvel, mary	When MARY MARVEL said "SHAZAM!" the letters did not have the same meaning as when Captain Marvel said the word. What did Mary's "SHAZAM!" mean?
marx, groucho	Give three consolation questions GROUCHO MARX asked the losers on *You Bet Your Life.*
masterson, bat	Now when The West was very young, what did those with too ready a trigger forget to figure on when confronting BAT MASTERSON?
matilda	Where did MATILDA run after she take me money?
mayor of the town	Who played the wise and solid mayor on the television series, *MAYOR OF THE TOWN?*
mcgee, fibber and molly	Who was the mayor on *FIBBER McGEE AND MOLLY?*

marvel, mary	The grace of Selena The strength of Hippolyta The skill of Ariadne The fleetness of Zephyrus The beauty of Aurora The wisdom of Minerva
marx, groucho	Who is buried in Grant's tomb? How long do you cook a three-minute egg? What's the color of an orange?
masterson, bat	His lightning cane (not to be confused with Hiram Holiday's [Wally Cox's] lightning umbrella)
matilda	Venezuela
mayor of the town	Thomas Mitchell
mcgee, fibber, and molly	Mayor La Trivia (a *very* nice name, we think)

mcguire, mickey	Who played MICKEY Mc-GUIRE, the tough little urchin in the Our Gang movies?
meet corliss archer	Who was CORLISS ARCHER's boyfriend? Who played him?
mickey mouse club	How did the Mouseketeers prepare for their daily Disney cartoon on the *MICKEY MOUSE CLUB?*
midnight, captain	What did CAPTAIN MIDNIGHT call his faithful plane? In the comics, what was Captain Midnight's secret identity and what was his occupation? Where was his laboratory?
midsummer night's dream, a	Who played Oberon, the king, in the film version of *A MIDSUMMER NIGHT'S DREAM?*
milquetoast, caspar	What was the name of CASPAR MILQUETOAST's comic strip?

mcguire, mickey	Mickey Rooney
meet corliss archer	Dexter
	Bobby Ellis (Corliss was played by Ann Baker.)
mickey mouse club	They said the magic words, "Meeska, Mooska, Mouseketeer—mouse cartoon time now is here."
midnight, captain	Silver Dart
	Captain Albright; "one of America's great inventors"
	Nevada
midsummer night's dream, a	Victor Jory, far removed from his usual hard-hitting characterizations
milquetoast, caspar	"The Timid Soul"

mineo, sal	SAL MINEO played Dino in ———————.
modern romances	Who was hostess of the daily television soap opera, *MODERN ROMANCES?*
monte cristo, count of	Who played the COUNT OF MONTE CRISTO on television?
mouse, mickey	Who was the police chief in MICKEY MOUSE's comic home town?
mr. first nighter	Who starred in *MR. FIRST NIGHTER?* What theater did they regularly attend?
mr. peabody and the mermaid	Who played the extraordinarily lucky fisherman in *MR. PEABODY AND THE MERMAID?*

211

mineo, sal	*Rebel Without a Cause*
modern romances	Martha Scott
monte cristo, count of	George Dolenz
mouse, mickey	Chief O'Hara (not a mouse but an Irishman)
mr. first nighter	Olan Soulé (succeeding Les Tremayne) and Barbara Luddie
	"The little theater just off Times Square"
mr. peabody and the mermaid	William Powell (Ann Blyth played the enchanting mermaid.)

m-squad	What was Lee Marvin's name in *M-SQUAD?*
	In what big city did he confront the elements of the underworld?
muffin man	Where does the MUFFIN MAN live?
mulligan, mickey	What was Mickey Rooney's occupation when he played MICKEY MULLIGAN in the television series, *Hey, Mulligan?*
	Who played his father?
mutt and jeff	What was Mutt's full name in the comic strip *MUTT AND JEFF?*
my favorite husband	Who starred in the television series *MY FAVORITE HUSBAND?*
my man godfrey	What did the butler, Godfrey (William Powell), do for his employers above and beyond the call of duty, in the film, *MY MAN GODFREY?*

m-squad	Lt. Frank Ballinger Chicago
muffin man	In Drury Lane
mulligan, mickey	He was a page in a television studio. Regis Toomey
mutt and jeff	Augustus P. Mutt
my favorite husband	Joan Caulfield, Barry Nelson
my man godfrey	He showed them what it was like to live on the other side of the tracks.

nbc matinee theater	Who was the host on the daily, hour-long *NBC MATINEE THEATER?*
nelson, jimmy	What were the names of JIMMY NELSON's boy and dog dummies?
	What song did the dog make famous?
ness, elliot	Who was ELLIOT NESS's Italian agent who was mowed down by a "dum-dum" bullet?
new orleans, the battle of	According to the song, "THE BATTLE OF NEW ORLEANS," how fast did the British run?
	Where did they run?
night at the opera, a	What song did Groucho Marx insert into the musicians' music for *Il Trovatore* in the film, *A NIGHT AT THE OPERA?*
97- pound weakling	*See* atlas, charles.

nbc matinee theater	John Conte
nelson, jimmy	Danny O'Day and Farfel "N-E-S-T-L-E-S— Nestles makes the very best Chawk-lit!"
ness, elliot	Joe Fucile (played by Keenan Wynn)
new orleans, the battle of	So fast that the hounds couldn't catch them, Down the Mississippi to the Gulf of Mexico
night at the opera, a	"Take Me Out to the Ball Game"

nov shmoz . . .

Complete the following: NOV SHMOZ ————.

With what comic strip was this phrase associated?

oakley, annie

Who played ANNIE OAKLEY in the original, non-musical film?

Who was Annie on television?

o'connor, donald

Who was DONALD O'CONNOR's partner on *The Donald O'Connor Show* and *Here Comes Donald?*

old lady vanishes, the

In *THE OLD LADY VANISHES,* what was the old lady's name?

100 men and a girl

How did Deanna Durbin and Dick Powell help the unemployed musicians, singers and dancers in *100 MEN AND A GIRL?*

nov shmoz . . .   Ka pop
                   "The Squirrel Cage"

oakley, annie   Barbara Stanwyck (The musical
                       version, Irving Berlin's *Annie
                       Get Your Gun,* starred Betty
                       Hutton.)
                   Gail Davis

o'connor,   Sidney Miller (who later went on
donald   to bigger and better things—
                       directing the Mouseketeers)

old lady   Mrs. Froy
vanishes

100 men and   They prodded them to put on a
a girl   show to earn money to take
                       themselves out of their de-
                       pression-time misery.

orchid, brother

What did Edward G. Robinson decide to do at the end of *BROTHER ORCHID?*

Who played the rich Texan who married Robinson's ex-girl-friend (played by Ann Soth-ern)?

passport to danger

What Latin-lover type played a government courier in *PASSPORT TO DANGER?*

piersall, jimmy

Who played JIMMY PIERSALL in *Fear Strikes Out?*

pizza pie

What is it when the moon hits your eye like a big PIZZA PIE?

orchid, brother	Enter a monastery Ralph Bellamy
passport to danger	Caesar Romero
piersall, jimmy	Anthony Perkins
pizza pie	That's *amore.*

plastic man

How did PLASTIC MAN attain his superhuman ability to stretch his body at will?

What was his name and occupation before he joined up with Woozy Winks to combat crime?

plainsman, the law of the

What was the name of the Indian marshal played by Michael Ansara on *THE LAW OF THE PLAINSMAN?*

Where was he educated?

What was the name of the actress who played the little girl he adopted?

plow that broke the plains, the

THE PLOW THAT BROKE THE PLAINS was a documentary about _____.

pooh, winnie the

What did Christopher Robin give WINNIE THE POOH for being a brave and courageous bear?

What was Pooh's favorite food?

What type of animal was Eyeore?

plastic man	A vat of acid fell on him, miraculously making him elastic.
	"Eel" O'Brien, a slippery but nonelastic criminal
plainsman, the law of the	Sam Buckhart; Harvard (He couldn't get into Columbia.)
	Gina Gillespie
plow that broke the plains, the	The unfortunate creation of the Dust Bowl
pooh, winnie the	A pencil case with the initials "P.B." (for Sir Pooh de Bear)
	"Hunny"
	A donkey

porridge, peas	How old is PEAS PORRIDGE in the pot?
preston, sgt.	What did SGT. PRESTON proclaim when he made an arrest?
pride of the family	Name the cast of the television series, *PRIDE OF THE FAMILY*.
pretend	When you're blue, how difficult is it to PRETEND you're happy?
professional father	Who starred in *PROFESSIONAL FATHER,* a situation comedy about a psychologist with his own child problems?
queen, ellery	Who starred on television as the author-detective ELLERY QUEEN?
queen, madame	MADAME QUEEN was ——'s girlfriend.

porridge, peas	Nine days (the same age as The Naughty Lady of Shady Lane)
preston, sgt.	"I arrest you in the name of the crown."
pride of the family	Paul Hartman, Fay Wray (of *King Kong* fame), Natalie Wood and Bobby Hiatt
pretend	It isn't very hard to do.
professional father	Steve Dunn and Barbara Billingsly (who later became Beaver Cleaver's mom)
queen, ellery	Hugh Marlow
queen, madame	Andrew H. Brown (Andy of *Amos 'n' Andy, q.v.*)

rabbit, harvey the	What was odd about HARVEY THE RABBIT?

Whose friend was he? |
| raft, george | GEORGE RAFT played a cop in his only television series. What was this series called? |
| rain | Two talking-picture versions of *RAIN* have been made. Who played Sadie Thompson in each? |
| raymond, roy | ROY RAYMOND appeared in "Detective Comics." What was his profession?

What was his wife's name? |
| restless gun | Who starred as a peripatetic gunhand in *RESTLESS GUN*? |
| rider, range | Who starred in the television series, *RANGE RIDER*? |
| riley, chester a. | Who played CHESTER A. RILEY's wife, daughter and son?

What was Riley's foreman's name?

Who starred as Riley on television before William Bendix? |

rabbit, harvey the	He was invisible. Mild-mannered Elwood P. Dowd's
raft, george	*I'm the Law*
rain	Joan Crawford and Rita Hayworth
raymond, roy	TV detective Karen
restless gun	John Payne
rider, range	Jock Mahoney (Dick West, his sidekick, went on to star in the series, *Buffalo Bill, Jr.*)
riley, chester a.	Marjorie Reynolds as Peg, Lugene Sanders as Babs, and Wesley Morgan as Junior Hank Hawkins, the pride and joy of Cunningham Aircraft Co. Jackie Gleason

rogers, buck
In what century did BUCK ROGERS operate?

rogers, roy
What was the name of the ranch on which ROY ROGERS lived and played?

room service
What expression did the hotel manager in *ROOM SERVICE* use to indicate his exasperation with the Marx Brothers?

saber, mark
Who portrayed the one-armed detective, MARK SABER, on television?

saint, the
What was THE SAINT's real name?

Who created this crafty sophisticate?

Who were The Saint's pesky American and British inspector friends?

rogers, buck	The 25th
rogers, roy	Double-R-Bar
room service	"Jumpin' butterballs!"

saber, mark	Donald Grey
saint, the	Simon Templar
	Leslie Charteris
	Inspector Fernac (U.S.) and Inspector Teale (G.B.)

salve
: What brand SALVE offered fantastic premiums to ambitious salesboys and salesgirls?

sawyer, buzz
: Who was the funny character in the comic strip, "BUZZ SAWYER"?

scarface
: Who starred as the ruthless criminal in *SCARFACE?*

schmidt, john j. j.
: His name is JOHN J. J. SCHMIDT. His name is my name, too. Whenever I go out, all the people start to shout my name. What does J. J. stand for?

seuss, doctor
: What was the name of the egg-hatching elephant created by DOCTOR SEUSS?

shadow, the
: What unique power did THE SHADOW possess?

Where did he acquire it?

Name four actors who played the knowledgeable crimefighter on radio.

sh-boom
: Who sang "SH-BOOM," one of the pre-Presley rock 'n' roll hits?

229

salve	Cloverine
sawyer, buzz	Roscoe Sweeney
scarface	Paul Muni
schmidt, john j.j.	Jacob Jingleheimer
seuss, dr.	Horton
shadow, the	The power to cloud men's minds On a trip to the Orient Orson Welles, Frank Readick, Bill Johnson, Brett Morrison
sh-boom	The Crewcuts

sheena	What was the name of the boy-friend of SHEENA, Queen of the Jungle?
	Who played Sheena on television?
simon, simple	What did the pieman ask SIMPLE SIMON to show him before he would let him taste his wares?
singing lady, the	Who was THE SINGING LADY?
single	What would happen to me if I were SINGLE again?
$64,000 question, the	What was the consolation prize for those who didn't get by all the plateaus on *THE $64,000 QUESTION?*
slaughter, texas john	TEXAS JOHN SLAUGHTER made them do what they ought'er. Why did they do it?
spectre, the	Who was THE SPECTRE and what was his mission?

sheena	Bob Irish McCalla
simon, simple	His penny (Indeed, alas, he hadn't any. And thus, we assume, he didn't get to taste the pieman's wares.)
singing lady	Ireene Wicker
single	My pockets would jingle.
$64,000 question	A brand-new Cadillac
slaughter, texas john	'Cause if they didn't they died.
spectre, the	Jim Corrigan, the detective, "whose mission is to rid the world of crime"

stage door canteen	In *STAGE DOOR CANTEEN,* Katharine Cornell did a scene from *Romeo and Juliet.* Who was Romeo?
star is born, a	Who starred in the original version of *A STAR IS BORN?*
stop the music	On *STOP THE MUSIC,* what sound told Bert Parks to flash his teeth and yell, "Stop the music!"
stratton, monte	Who played the film role of the heroic, one-legged baseball pitcher, **MONTE STRATTON?**
strawberry blonde	What was Biff Grime's (James Cagney's) line of work in *STRAWBERRY BLONDE?*
	Who played his wife?
stories of the century	Who starred in the western series, *STORIES OF THE CENTURY?*
	What was the name of his lovely assistant?

stage door canteen	Lon McCallister
star is born, a	Janet Gaynor and Fredric March
stop the music	The ring of a telephone
stratton, monte	Jimmy Stewart
strawberry blonde	Dentistry Olivia de Havilland
stories of the century	Jim Davis, playing the role of a railroad investigator Frankie Adams

studio 57   What did the "57" stand for in *STUDIO 57?*

sugarfoot   Where could you find SUGAR-FOOT?

Who starred in *Sugarfoot?*

sunday, our gal   Where did OUR GAL SUNDAY live?

Where was she born?

superboy   In what little American town was SUPERBOY reared by the Kents?

suspense   Who was the announcer on *SUSPENSE?*

Who sponsored this program?

swayze, john cameron   Who was the weatherman on JOHN CAMERON SWAYZE's news broadcasts?

sweeney and sons   What was the companion comic strip to "SWEENEY AND SONS?"

studio 57	The number of varieties of Heinz foods
sugarfoot	On the side of law and order from the Mexicali border to the rolling hills of Arkansas
	Will Hutchins
sunday, our gal	Black Swan Hall
	Cripple Creek, Colo.
superboy	Smallville (As many young men are wont to do, he soon left Smallville to find his fame and fortune in Metropolis, not far from Gotham City.)
suspense	Harlow Wilcox
	Autolite
swayze, john cameron	P. J. Hoff
sweeney and sons	"Jinglets"

tales of the
texas rangers
Who led the rangers down the street double-file at the opening of *TALES OF THE TEXAS RANGERS?*

tarzan
Who played TARZAN's son (Boy) in the Johnny Weissmuller film series?

terries and
fermies
See uncle $crooge.

terrific, tom
What was the name of TOM TERRIFIC's dog?

Who was Tom's arch-enemy?

texan, the
Who starred in *THE TEXAN?*

three godfathers
To whom was *THREE GODFATHERS* dedicated?

tightrope
Where did Mike Connors, as an undercover agent, always keep his revolver on *TIGHTROPE?*

tim tyler's luck
In the serial, *TIM TYLER'S LUCK,* what was everyone trying to discover?

tales of the texas rangers	Harry Lauter and Willard Parker
tarzan	Johnny Sheffield (Now, whatever happened to *him?*)
terrific, tom	Mighty Manfred Crabby Appleton
texan, the	Rory Calhoun
three godfathers	Harry Carey, Sr., whose son, Harry, Jr., was in the picture
tightrope	In a holster at the back of his belt
tim tyler's luck	The elephants' burial ground, with its abundance of ivory, the source of much mayhem (Tusk, tusk!)

titanic	For what did they build the ship *TITANIC?*
	What happened when the great ship went down (to the bottom of the sea)?
toasties, post	According to the jingle, what's the difference between eating POST TOASTIES for breakfast and for snacks?
today	Who were the male and female chimps on the *TODAY* show on television?
toonerville trolley	What was the full name of the comic strip that tells the story of the TOONERVILLE TROLLEY and the inhabitants of Toonerville?
	Describe the powerful Katrinka's boyfriend.
torch, the human	Who was THE HUMAN TORCH's sidekick?
trackdown	In *TRACKDOWN,* how did Robert Culp, as Ranger Hobey Gilman, describe Texas Rangers?

titanic	To sail the ocean blue (But the water did go through.)
	Husbands and wives, little children lost their lives.
toasties, post	For breakfast they're dandy, for snacks they're quite handy. (You can also eat 'em like candy.)
today	J. Fredd Muggs and the lovely Phoebe B. Beebe
toonerville trolley	"The Toonerville Trolley That Meets All Trains"
	He was a cigar-smoking dwarf.
torch, the human	Toro
trackdown	"They could ride like Mexicans, shoot like Tennesseans and fight like the very devil."

tracy, dick	What was DICK TRACY's wife's maiden name?
	Who played D. T. on television and in the movies?
troubleshooters, the	What professionals were depicted in *THE TROUBLESHOOTERS?*
	Who starred in that show?
tubby	What comic-book feature section never failed to contain the immortal passage, "TUBBY thinks he's so smart."
twelve angry men	Who played the conciliatory foreman of the jury in *TWELVE ANGRY MEN?*
	What was the charge?
	What was the verdict?
twentieth century	Who starred opposite John Barrymore, playing a temperamental director, as a temperamental actress in *TWENTIETH CENTURY?*

241

tracy, dick	Tess Trueheart
	Ralph Byrd
troubleshooters, the	Construction engineers
	Keenan Wynn and Bob Matthias (the Olympic decathlon champ)
tubby	"Lulu's Diry"
twelve angry men	Martin Balsam
	Murder in the first degree
	Not guilty
twentieth century	Carole Lombard

uncle $crooge

How does the neckwear of the Terries differ from that of the Fermies?

urania, scientific city of

In what movie serial did a cowboy star descend into the center of the Earth to do battle with the inhabitants of the SCIENTIFIC CITY OF URANIA?

Who was the cowboy?

What did he call his ranch?

vic and sade

Where did VIC AND SADE live?

wagon train

Who was the original wagonmaster on *WAGON TRAIN?*

wanderer, the happy

What does *THE HAPPY WANDERER* carry on his back?

What does he sing?

uncle $crooge	The Terries wear bow ties; the Fermies wear four-in-hands.
urania, scienti- fic city of	*Phantom Empire* Gene Autry Radio Ranch (the home of his daily musical radio show)
vic and sade	In the "little house halfway up in the next block"
wagon train	Ward Bond (Robert Horton played his right-hand man.)
wanderer, the happy	A knapsack "Valderee, valdera . . ."

war	What product went to WAR?
wednesday night fights	What was the name of the WEDNESDAY NIGHT FIGHTS sponsored by Pabst beer?
wells fargo, tales of	Who starred in *TALES OF WELLS FARGO?*
wences, señor	What was the name of the hand-puppet SENOR WENCES used to manipulate on Ed Sullivan's popular stage?
western, the	On the television series, *THE WESTERN,* starring Brian Keith, what was the name of the professional gambler?
	Who played him?
wheaties	Have you tried WHEATIES?
when a girl marries	Who was the star of the soap opera, *WHEN A GIRL MARRIES?*
	Who played her husband, Harry?

war	Lucky Strike Green
wednesday night fights	Blue Ribbon Bouts
wells fargo, tales of	Dale Robertson
wences, señor	Johnny (pronounced "Yonny" . . . 'Tsall right? . . . 'Tsall right!)
western, the	Burgundy Smith John Dehner (radio's Paladin)
wheaties	Yes or no.
when a girl marries	Mary Jane Higby (as Joan Davis) Robert Haag

wife, backstage	What were the names of BACK-STAGE WIFE and her actor husband?
wilbur	Who were the two girls in WIL-BUR's comic-book life?
winchell, paul	What were the names of PAUL WINCHELL's two main dummies?
	Who was his musical director on *The Winchell-Mahoney Club?*
wind in the willows	In the story, *WIND IN THE WILLOWS,* what was the name of Mr. Toad's residence?
woman's face, a	Whose face was scarred in the film, *A WOMAN'S FACE?*
world of mr. sweeney, the	Who played the storekeeper in *THE WORLD OF MR. SWEENEY?*
wonder woman	What were WONDER WOMAN's four outstanding attributes?
	Who was her boyfriend?

wife, backstage	Mary and Larry Noble
wilbur	Laurie and Linda
winchell, paul	Jerry Mahoney and Knucklehead Smiff
	Milton De Lugg
wind in the willows	Toad Hall
woman's face, a	Joan Crawford's
world of mr. sweeney, the	Charlie Ruggles
wonder woman	The beauty of Aphrodite The wisdom of Athena The strength of Hercules And the swiftness of Mercury (among other things)
	Steve Trevor (among other guys)

x	How many points is an "X" tile worth in Scrabble?
x, comrade	At the end of the movie, *COMRADE X,* Clark Gable took his two new Russian friends to a baseball game. What teams were playing?
x, dr.	Who played DR. X in *The Mysterious Dr. X?*
yankees, n.y.	What two actors portrayed N.Y. YANKEES Lou Gehrig and Babe Ruth in the movies?
yellow rose of texas, the	What two girls are unfavorably compared to THE YELLOW ROSE OF TEXAS in the song?

x	Eight
x, comrade	The Brooklyn Dodgers and the Cincinnati Reds
x, dr.	Humphrey Bogart (believe it or not)
yankees, n.y.	Gary Cooper played Larruping Lou and William Bendix played the Sultan of Swat.
yellow rose of texas, the	Clementine and Rosalie

you'll never get rich	What was the name of Master Sgt. Ernie Bilko's commanding officer in *YOU'LL NEVER GET RICH*?
	Who played him?
	What were the names of the sergeants in charge of mess, communications and supplies?
	Where did Bilko move his entire camp when he felt that Roosevelt, Kans., was cramping his style?
young widder brown	What doctor wanted to marry YOUNG WIDDER BROWN?
zaback, florian	What musical instrument did FLORIAN ZABACK play on his own television series, modeled after Liberace's?
	Liberace's brother was George. Name Zaback's.
zebra kid, the	What wrestler billed himself as "THE ZEBRA KID"?

you'll never get rich	Col. Hall
	Paul Ford
	Ridzic, Grover and Pendleton
	Grove City, Calif.
young widder brown	Anthony Loring

zaback, florian	Violin
	He didn't have one—at least not on television.
zebra kid, the	Lenny Montana

ziegfield, the great	Who played the title role in *THE GREAT ZIEGFIELD?*
	Who played his wife, Billie Burke?
z-ro, captain	Where did CAPTAIN Z-RO go for his adventures?

TRIVIA MATCHING QUIZ 1

Match the bad guy to the good guy:

1. Archie
2. Happy Tooth
3. The Lone Ranger
4. Sluggo
5. Dick Tracy
6. Flash Gordon
7. Mickey Mouse
8. Ben Gay
9. Crusader Rabbit
10. Sherlock Holmes

Peter Pain
Pruneface
Dudley Nightshade
Professor Moriarty
Mr. Tooth Decay
Butch Cavendish
Butch
Reggie
Ming the Merciless
Black Pete

TRIVIA MATCHING QUIZ 2

Match the horse to the correct western hero:

1. Tom Mix
2. Gene Autry
3. Dan Reid
4. Roy Rogers
5. Hopalong Cassidy
6. Bob Steele
7. Ken Maynard
8. Wild Bill Hickok
9. Tonto
10. Sgt. Preston

Topper
Trigger
Rusty
Scout
Champion
Rex
Buckshot
Tarzan
Victor
Tony

ziegfield, the great	William Powell
	Myrna Loy
z-ro, captain	Back in time, via a marvelous time machine

ANSWERS TO TRIVIA MATCHING QUIZ 1

1. Reggie
2. Mr. Tooth Decay
3. Butch Cavendish
4. Butch
5. Pruneface
6. Ming the Merciless
7. Black Pete
8. Peter Pain
9. Dudley Nightshade
10. Professor Moriarty

ANSWERS TO TRIVIA MATCHING QUIZ 2

1. Tony
2. Champion
3. Victor
4. Trigger
5. Topper
6. Rusty
7. Tarzan
8. Buckshot
9. Scout
10. Rex

TRIVIA MATCHING QUIZ 3

Match the description or title to the appropriate character:

1. Captain Marvel   "King of the Wild Frontier"
2. Jack Armstrong   "World's Greatest Body Builder"
3. The Lone Ranger   "Lonesome"
4. Davy Crockett   "Mild-mannered reporter"
5. Dr. Sivana   "The All-American Boy"
6. Charles Atlas   "The daring and resourceful masked rider of the plains"
7. George F. Jowett   "The friendly ghost"
8. Clark Kent   "The World's Most Perfectly Developed Man"
9. George Gobel   "The world's mightiest mortal"
10. Caspar   "The world's wickedest scientist"

TRIVIA MATCHING QUIZ 4

Match the pet to the proper master:

1. George and Marian Kirby   Yukon King
2. Timmy   Macdougal
3. Mrs. Davis   Polly
4. Nick and Nora Charles   Neil
5. Jack Benny   Rin Tin Tin
6. Sgt. Preston   Asta
7. Beanie   Squeaky
8. Rusty B. Company   Lassie
9. Smilin' Ed   Minerva
10. Mr. Boynton   Cecil

ANSWERS TO TRIVIA
MATCHING QUIZ 3

1. "The world's mightiest mortal"
2. "The All-American Boy"
3. "The daring and resourceful masked rider of the plains"
4. "King of the Wild Frontier"
5. "The world's wickedest scientist"
6. "The World's Most Perfectly Developed Man"
7. "World's Greatest Body Builder"
8. "Mild-mannered reporter"
9. "Lonesome"
10. "The friendly ghost"

ANSWERS TO TRIVIA
MATCHING QUIZ 4

1. Neil
2. Lassie
3. Minerva
4. Asta
5. Polly
6. Yukon King
7. Cecil
8. Rin Tin Tin
9. Squeaky
10. Macdougal

TRIVIA MATCHING QUIZ 5

Match the actor to the music-world figure he portrayed:

1. Cole Porter	Steve Allen
2. Jerome Kern	Clifton Webb
3. Tommy Dorsey	Robert Walker
4. George Gershwin	Keefe Brasselle
5. Benny Goodman	Mickey Rooney
6. Eddie Cantor	Tommy Dorsey
7. Al Jolson	Robert Alda
8. John Philip Sousa	Larry Parks
9. George M. Cohan	Cary Grant
10. Lorenz Hart	James Cagney

WHO SAID?

1. "Dwat that wabbit!"
2. "Hey there, Ralphie boy!"
3. "I remember San Francisco . . . the little house on Steiner Street . . ."
4. "Howdy, bub."
5. "Ah, yes, it's good news tonight."
6. "I don't know, Angie. What do *you* want to do tonight?"
7. "You betchum!"
8. "Kowabonga!"
9. " 'Twas beauty that killed the beast."
10. "Pluck your magic twanger, Froggie!"
11. "Holy moley!"
12. "Heal! Heal!"
13. "You know, Louie, this could be the start of a beautiful friendship."
14. "Page two."
15. "Rosalie, come in and get dressed. I've got you laid out on the bed."

ANSWERS TO TRIVIA MATCHING QUIZ 5

1. Cary Grant
2. Robert Walker
3. Tommy Dorsey
4. Robert Alda
5. Steve Allen
6. Keefe Brasselle
7. Larry Parks
8. Clifton Webb
9. James Cagney
10. Mickey Rooney

ANSWERS TO "WHO SAID . . . ?

1. Elmer Fudd
2. Ed Norton, Ralph Kramden's friend and neighbor
3. Kathryn, Mama's eldest daughter
4. Titus Moody, New England's delegate to Allen's Alley
5. Gabriel Heatter
6. Ernest Borgnine, as Marty
7. Little Beaver, Red Ryder's Tonto
8. Howdy Doody's faithful Indian companion, Chief Thunderthud
9. Carl Denham, King Kong's captor
10. Smilin' Ed McConnell and, later, Andy Devine, who changed Smilin' Ed's Gang into Andy's Gang
11. The Captains Marvel
12. Oral Roberts
13. Humphrey Bogart as Rick in *Casablanca*
14. Paul Harvey
15. Molly Goldberg

TWENTY TRIVIA QUESTIONS FOR THE CONNOISSEUR

Here is a collection of twenty very difficult questions. A black belt for Trivia expertness if you can answer ten or more. You may not bring an expert into the booth with you, but you *may* come back next week.

1. Once upon a time there was a television program that daily telecast an actual wedding ceremony. Name it.
2. Complete the line: "I don't want her, you can have her. . . ."
3. Who lived at Painted Valley Ranch?
4. What did Herself Muldoon, Miss Mizzou and Madame Lynx have in common?
5. Who manufactured the safe in which $crooge McDuck kept his zillions?
6. In what movie did Clark Gable and Loretta Young both play mayors?
7. In *The Petrified Forest,* Leslie Howard gave Bette Davis a book of poems. Whose poems?
8. What was the name of the Saturday afternoon radio quiz hosted by Arlene Francis and Bill Cullen?
9. What movie actors first played Superman, Batman and Captain Marvel?
10. What was Dr. Sivana's daughter's name?
11. In *Mr. Deeds Goes to Town,* what musical instrument did Gary Cooper play with the town band at the railroad station? What song did they play?
12. Give the names of Henry and Fanny Barbour's children.
13. Bobby Diamond, Peter Graves and William Fawcett starred in _____.

ANSWERS TO 20 TRIVIA QUESTIONS FOR THE CONNOISSEUR

1. *Bride and Groom*
2. "She's too fat for me."
3. Red Ryder
4. All three of these lovely ladies once played a part in the adventures of Steve Canyon.
5. The Oso Safe Co.
6. *Key to the City*
7. François Villon's
8. *Fun for All*
9. Kirk Allen, Louis Wilson, Tom Tyler
10. Beautia
11. Tuba; "For He's a Jolly Good Fellow"
12. Paul, Hazel, Jack, and the twins, Clifford and Claudia
13. *Fury*

14. In what movie did Artur Rubinstein play the piano? Isaac Stern, the violin?

15. What song asks the question, "How do you make a chicken sneeze?"

16. Two brothers appeared in the film version of *How Green Was My Valley*. Name them.

17. Who played Emmy Slattery, the poor white trash, in *Gone With The Wind?*

18. What was the odor Bogart smelled in *Dead Reckoning?*

19. Who often said, "Aren't we devils?" and under what circumstances?

20. What do the following have in common: *The Three Musketeers, Ivanhoe, The Count of Monte Cristo, The Last of the Mohicans, Moby Dick, A Tale of Two Cities?*

14. *I've Always Loved You; Humoresque*

15. "Tell Me a Story"

16. Arthur Shields and Barry Fitzgerald

17. Isabel Jewel

18. Jasmine

19. Ralph Edwards, after surprising the guest of the evening on *This Is Your Life*

20. They are the first six works in the "Classics Illustrated" series of comic books.

DOUBLE-TROUBLE TRIVIA

INSTRUCTIONS: Fill in the answers to the questions on the next two pages in the blanks provided. Then transfer the letters from the numbered blanks to the appropriate squares on the Trivia grid below.
The completed puzzle will produce 26 tugs of the heart and one of the most famous and stirring quotations in the Trivia tradition.

		h 1	i 2	y 3	r 4	j 5	i 6		v 7	x 8
g 9	j 10	t 11		d 12	h 13	w 14	t 15	e 16	a 17	u 18
g 19		c 20	s 21	r 22	a 23	j 24	f 25	g 26	q 27	u 28
v 29		b 30	u 31	d 32	p 33	w 34	v 35	g 36	h 37	f 38
e 39	i 40	r 41		e 42		i 43	i 44	u 45	e 46	h 47	u 48
k 49	i 50	j 51	p 52		e 53	f 54	u 55	d 56	r 57	z 58
	p 59	d 60	r 61	a 62		d 63	g 64	u 65	i 66	p 67
m 68	h 69	r 70	p 71	k 72	j 73	s 74	t 75	o 76	v 77	
e 78		l 79	v 80	g 81	p 82	i 83	y 84	g 85	v 86	n 87
e 88	u 89		p 90	a 91	y 92	g 93	b 94	w 95	f 96
x 97		d 98	r 99	v 100		d 101	u 102	g 103	p 104	f 105
t 106		g 107		c 108	u 109	l 110	r 111	g 112	d 113	z 114
	g 115		x 116	h 117	z 118	d 119	n 120	e 121	v 122	e 123
	k 124	d 125	w 126	a 127	g 128	t 129	s 130	n 131		

a. *What the worms play on your snout*   — — — — — — —
    62 17   91   23 127

b. *The fat Fleer's Bubble Gum kid.*   — — —
    30 94

(*Continued on next page*)

c. Dragnet *star*.

— — — —
108 20

d. *"Animal, vegetable or mineral" quiz show.*

— — — — —
63 32 60   98

— — — — — — —
125 56 12 113   119

—
101

e. *A dark, secluded place where you won't find your Uncle Max and everyone you know.*

— — — — — —
39   88 53   46 123

— — — — — —
121 16   78   42

f. *Starred in both*—Date with an Angel *and* Life with Elizabeth.

— — — —
54   38 105

— — — —
96 25

g. *Where cigarette trees, soda-water fountains and lemonade springs can be found.*

— — — — — —
85   19   128   93

— — — — —
107 81   103

— — — — — —
26   36   9 112

h. *A short, red-haired fellow created by Ernie Bushmiller.*

— — — —
13   69 117

— — — — —
1   47

i. Long Long Trailer *leading lady.*

— — — — — —
66   50   43

— — — —
40   83

j. *Tinkerbell's land.*

— — — — — — —
10   51 24   73   5

—

k. *Memories are made of _____.*

— — — —
49   72 124

l. *Mrs. Miniver.*

— — — — —
6   110

— — — — —
2   79 44

m. A Date with _____.

— — — —
68

n. _____ *Wiggly.*

— — — — —
87 131   37 120

264

o. *Penrod's pal.*
  — — —
  76

p. *What somebody bad stole.*
  — —
  33

— — — — — —
52 71   104   82

— — —
67   90 59

q. A Bell for ____.
  — — — —
  64   115   27

r. *Peg   Lynch   and   Alan Bunce.*
  — — — — —
  4 99   22   41 111

— — — — —
61 70   57

s. *What the McGuire sisters had in the morning, in the evening and at suppertime.*
  — — — —
  21 74 130

t. *Be-bop-a-loo-la,* ____.
  — — — — — —
  75   15 106   129

— — —
11

u. *It gives me a thrill to wake up in the morning* ____.
  — —
  48

— — — — —
31 45 102   18

— — — —
    28 89

— — — —
109 65 55

v. *Film that marked Sinatra's comeback.*
  — — — — — — —
  35   86   29   100

— —
122

— — — — — — —
  77   80 7

w. ____ Young's Family.
— — — — —
126   95   14 34

x. The Right to ____.
— — — — — — —
8   116   97

y. *Nanook of the North.*
— — — — —
84 3   92

z. *The greatest pancake eater of them all.*
— — — —
114 118   58

ANSWERS TO DOUBLE-TROUBLE TRIVIA

a. PINOCHLE
b. PUD
c. WEBB
d. TWENTY QUESTIONS
e. HERNANDO'S HIDEAWAY
f. BETTY WHITE
g. BIG ROCK CANDY MOUNTAIN
h. PHIL FUMBLE
i. LUCILLE BALL
j. NEVERNEVER
k. THIS
l. GREER GARSON
m. JUDY
n. UNCLE
o. SAM
p. DE WEDDING BELL
q. ADANO
r. ETHEL AND ALBERT
s. SUGAR
t. SHE'S MY BABY
u. ON MOCKINGBIRD HILL
v. FROM HERE TO ETERNITY
w. PEPPER
x. HAPPINESS
y. ESKIMO
z. SAMBO

FASTER THAN A SPEEDING BULLET . . . MORE POWERFUL THAN A LOCOMOTIVE . . . ABLE TO LEAP TALL BUILDINGS AT A SINGLE BOUND . . . LOOK! . . . UP IN THE SKY! . . . IT'S A BIRD! . . . IT'S A PLANE! . . . IT'S *SUPERMAN!!*

Answers for Trivia
Photoquiz

1. *A Night at the Opera;* Allan Jones and Kitty Carlisle
2. "When the Moon Comes Over the Mountain" and "God Bless America"
3. "A fiery horse with the speed of light"
4. Nick and Nora Charles, Peter Lawford and Phyllis Kirk, Asta
5. The King of the Clay People, Flash Gordon and Dr. Zarkov—discussing how to lift the curse from the Clay people (a rather sticky business)
6. Boy and Cheetah
7. Spanky, Buckwheat, Porky, Alfalfa, and the lovely Darla
8. *To Have and Have Not*—Martinique
9. Duncan Renaldo (The Cisco *Keed*)
10. Bram Stoker
11. Carl Denham, played by Robert Armstrong

ANSWERS TO TRIVIA PHOTOQUIZ

12. TONY MARVIN

13. Bowling with Ralph Kramden (playing pool was a close second)

14. Nyoka; perils

15. He used a bullwhip to disarm opponents as often as he used a gun. His name—Lash LaRue.

16. *b.* Argentina (birthplace of Antonino Rocca)

17. Clark Gable and Claudette Colbert in *It Happened One Night*

18. William Boyd (Hopalong Cassidy)

19. Tex Ritter ("The Singing Cowboy")

20. *e.* Inspector La Strade

21. *a.* Eddie and Debbie

22. *d.* The Mummy

23. *c.* Sons of the Desert

Photos 13, 16, 18, 19, 20, 21 courtesy of Steve Sallay, 339 W. 44th Street, New York, N.Y.